COLOUR CLASSI

YELLOW

BABUL
CHAMPAK
CORALWOOD
DHAMAN
DHAURA
GUMHAR
INDIAN KINO *
INDIAN LABURNUM
JAVA CASSIA
PORTIA TREE
SCREW PINE (male flowers)
TAMARIND
YELLOW OLEANDER
YELLOW SILK COTTON

PINK/RED

AFRICAN TULIP
ASHOKA
BANYAN (ripe fruits)
BODULA
BURMESE PINK CASSIA
CANNON BALL
CORAL JASMINE (only the stalk)
CYCAS (male cone)
EAST INDIAN SCREW
FLAME OF FOREST
GULAR (ripe fruit)
GULMOHUR
...ORAL
...NGLI BADAM
KAMALA (ripe fruit)
PAGODA TREE
PULA
RAIN TREE
SILK COTTON
TRUMPET FLOWER

PURPLE/LILAC

CAMEL HOOF
GIANT MILKWEED
KARANJ
PERSIAN LILAC
QUEEN'S FLOWER
TRUMPET FLOWER

GREEN

BEEFWOOD *
BOTTLE PALM *
CHRISTMAS TREE *
JACK FRUIT *
JAVA FIG
MAST TREE
PALMYRA PALM *
PEEPAL
PUTRANJIVA
ROUGH LEAVED FIG

FIELD GUIDE TO THE COMMON TREES OF INDIA

FIELD GUIDE TO THE COMMON TREES OF INDIA

P.V. Bole *and* Yogini Vaghani

Illustrations
Yogini Vaghani

Published for
WORLD WIDE FUND FOR NATURE-INDIA

OXFORD UNIVERSITY PRESS
Bombay Delhi Calcutta Madras

Oxford University Press
Oxford New York Toronto
Delhi Bombay Calcutta Madras Karachi
Pataling Jaya HongKong Singapore Tokyo
Nairobi Dar es Salaam
Melbourne Auckland
and associates in
Berlin Ibadan

First published 1986
Reprinted with corrections and new illustrations 1988
Reprinted 1989

Phototypeset by South End Typographics, Pondicherry,
printed by Prakash Desai, Mayuresh Printers, Goregaon (E),
Bombay 400 063 and published by S. K. Mookerjee, Oxford
University Press, Oxford House, Apollo Bunder, Bombay 400 039.

Acknowledgement

The World Wildlife Fund–India are grateful to the Sheth Purshotamdas Thakurdas and Divaliba Charitable Fund for financing the publication of this work.

Preface

he purpose of this compact handbook is to assist amateur nature vers who may not have formal training in botanical studies but are nd of hiking and trekking in the plains and foothills; who are struck y and inquisitive about the richness and beauty of the tree life that rrounds them both in the city and countryside.

Each of the trees described and drawn here has its season of lendour at one time of the year or another, often more than once or roughout the year. This may not necessarily be when it is in full oom; it could occur when fresh new leaves appear or even when it is afless. A regular observer who has trained his eyes to notice and preciate the tree life that surrounds him will not forget the extra-dinary sense of joy and exhileration that the trees he sees inspire hen at their best. If they are inquisitive about the individual haracteristics of these trees, about their life and habitat, the first step ould be to learn to recognize them by their common names and link ese with their scientific nomenclature.* The latter would give them cess to the vast storehouse of scholarly literature on the subject ould they so wish. There is an international system of nomenclature y which plants are recognizable all over the world and all floristic gions have scientific literature on their flora.

In a country as vast as India there are several thousand species of ees. This work treats only a little over a hundred of these, the mmonest encountered in the Indian plains and foothills. Some of ese are not indigenous to India but have become so popular that ey must be considered an intrinsic part of our landscape and have erefore been included. There are undoubtedly many other common ees, which for want of space could not be included, but our aim has en to include as representative a selection as possible.

The Key that prefaces the book, and is indeed a unique feature of , is intended as a bridge between the tree as the user observes it in e field and easy location of the relevant, more detailed description, in e text. It groups together trees with similar physical characteristics d, with the aid of pictorial symbols and thumbnail verbal sketches, dicates the possible sections of the text that relate to them.

Each description of a tree in the text is amplified by line drawings f the stem, leaves and flowers. Coloured illustrations have been

No up-to-date validity is claimed for the scientific names used in the book. hey have been selected to facilitate reference to standard regional floristic orks or reference volumes such as *The Wealth of India* (CSIR, New Delhi) here further information about their uses, distribution and silvicultural pects may be obtained.

dispensed with, partly due to the high cost and partly because it is ve
difficult to faithfully reproduce in print the exact nuances of colour
a living tree which appears different with every change of light a
shade.

At the end of the book there is a detailed glossary of terms wi
which the user may not be wholly familiar, including relatively simp
things like *flower* or *fruit* to indicate the roles, as against me
appearance, which various parts of a tree play in its biological cycle.
select list of books for further reference and a comprehensive ind
listing all the English and vernacular names are also include
Vernacular names have been included because the authors are co
vinced that they are useful not only for identification but also
enable the enthusiast to gather more first-hand information fro
people living in the area of provenance. However, both the spelli
and phonetic transcription of these names, and even the nam
themselves, will vary almost from one district to another. There are
standardized Indian local names for trees and, therefore, only five
seven out of a possible twenty or more names have had to be selecte
from the *Wealth of India* (op. cit.) and other similar published wor
to represent the eastern, northern, southern and western regions
India. The authors will be grateful if users of the book suggest mo
widely prevalent or appropriate names for particular regions.
future editions of this work it may be possible and desirable to use t
Devnagari script to indicate the exact pronunciation of local name
We feel there is a great need to standardize regional names of plants.

Many scholars and nature lovers have been struck by the beau
and almost mystic allure of Indian trees. It was impossible for us
resist reproducing some of their vivid reactions to lighten the tersene
of our brief descriptions. We are grateful to them.

Finally, it is suggested that those readers who are anxious to lear
more about the plant life around them should, besides consulting t
books listed at the end of this one, cultivate contacts with the Botar
Departments of local colleges or universities or the head of t
relevant circle of the Botanical Survey of India who have the experti
and staff to identify all local plants.

Our purpose in writing and illustrating this book will have bee
well served if it creates a greater awareness amongst our reade
about the richness and fascination of our natural heritage, and t
value of preserving and enlarging it. We are convinced that individu
interest, effort and awareness will have as great if not greater impa
on the movement for conservation than the 'high power' conferenc
and seminars we hear of every now and again attended by 'hig
powered' people!

Bombay
15 October 1985

P.V. Bo
YOGINI VAGHA

Contents

Key to the Identification of Trees

To use the key

1. Select a small branch of the tree you wish to identify. Avoid freaks.
2. It is necessary to observe and examine the twig carefully. If possible, use a magnifying glass (10 X).
3. Examine the leaves carefully, their arrangement, nerves, shape, leaf stalk, margin, apex and the type of leaf—simple or compound.
4. Start at the top of the next page.
5. Proceed step by step, considering the alternatives under each symbol.
6. When you have made the final choice, compare the twig with the illustration and check the description of the plant given in the text on the given page.
7. It is necessary to learn the significance and meaning of terms like alternate, opposite, simple, compound leaves; trifoliate, digitate, pinnate, bipinnate, tripinnate and stipules. (Refer to the glossary at the end of the book for this.)

NOTE: The Arabic page numbers in the body of the Key leading the user to the symbols refer to the bold arabic numbers 1–9 on the upper right-hand side of the pages of the Key. Those used in conjunction with proper names of trees refer to the relevant page number of the main text.

SYNOPSIS OF THE KEY

(*Contd. on next page*)

TRUNK BARK CRACKED (not flaky)

- Leaves simple xix 
  - Leaves opposite with stipules
  - Leaves opposite without stipules
  - Leaves alternate
    - stipules present
    - stipules absent
      - leaves lobed
      - leaves unlobed
- Leaves compound

SECTION I

UNBRANCHED TREES

or trees which have straight veins,
i.e. Palms, Bamboos, Cycas and Pandanus

If the tree is unbranched or with prominent jointed stems, see symbol 

- Leaves large, wedge-shaped, resembling the tail fin of a fish, see *Fish-tail Palm* on *p*. 43.
- Leaves fan shaped, trunk, covered with circular leaf scars, see *Palmyra Palm* on *p*. 85.
- Leaves feather-like, trunk covered with circular leaf scars like rings, see *Coconut Palm* on *p*. 29.
- Leaves feather-like, trunk narrow at base, bulging above resembling a bottle, generally cultivated, see *Bottle Palm* on *p*. 19.
- Leaves with short spines on stalk, tip of leaflets have sharp points, trunk rough with persistent leaf bases, see *Wild Date palm* on *p*. 107.
- Grass like woody plants with cylindrical hollow, prominently jointed stems, see *Bamboo* on *p*. 11.
- Leaves strap-like, with spines on margin, mostly with aerial stilt roots, see *Screw Pine* on *p*. 99.
- Leaves thick, glossy-green, resembling those of palms, trunk usually unbranched, see *Cycas Tree* on *p*. 33.

SECTION II

BRANCHED TREES ARMED WITH SPINE, THORNS PRICKLES, ETC.

If the tree is branched start with the symbol  on *p*. 1.

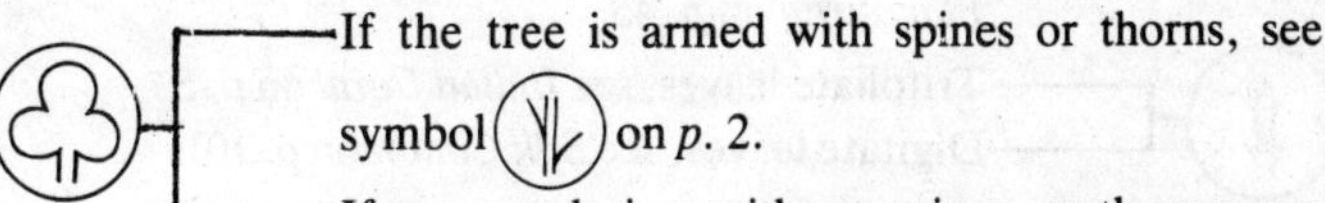

- If the tree is armed with spines or thorns, see symbol on *p*. 2.
- If unarmed, i.e. without spines or thorns, see symbol on *p*. 3.

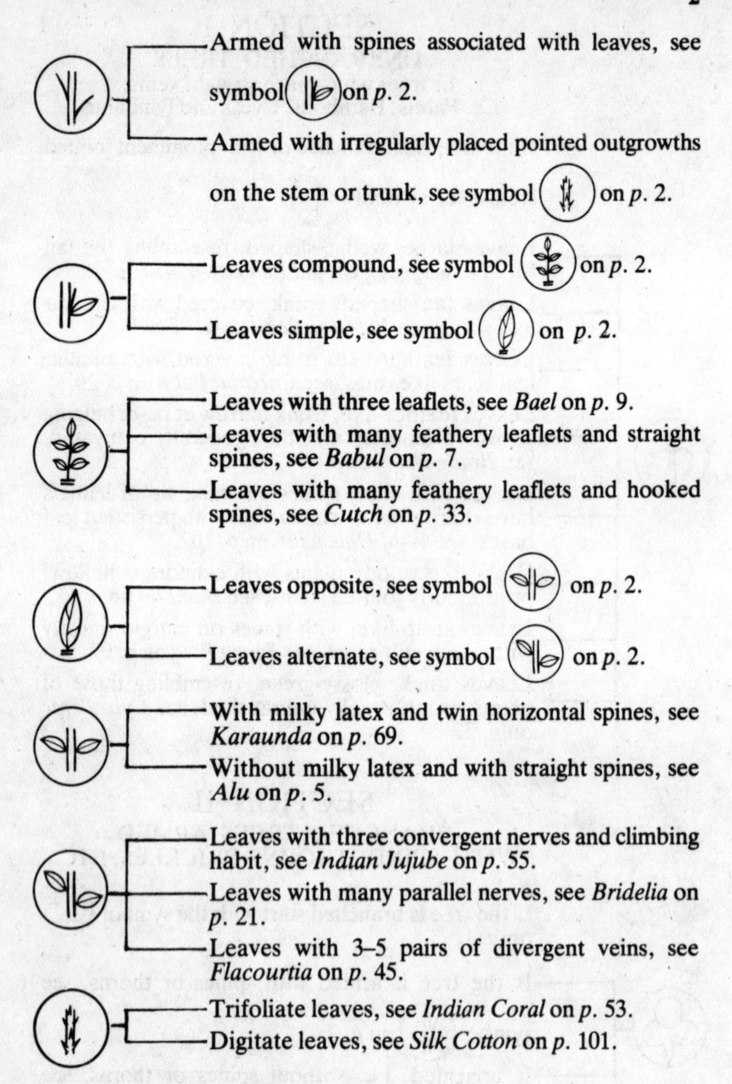

Armed with spines associated with leaves, see symbol (symbol) on p. 2.

Armed with irregularly placed pointed outgrowths on the stem or trunk, see symbol (symbol) on p. 2.

Leaves compound, see symbol (symbol) on p. 2.

Leaves simple, see symbol (symbol) on p. 2.

Leaves with three leaflets, see *Bael* on p. 9.

Leaves with many feathery leaflets and straight spines, see *Babul* on p. 7.

Leaves with many feathery leaflets and hooked spines, see *Cutch* on p. 33.

Leaves opposite, see symbol (symbol) on p. 2.

Leaves alternate, see symbol (symbol) on p. 2.

With milky latex and twin horizontal spines, see *Karaunda* on p. 69.

Without milky latex and with straight spines, see *Alu* on p. 5.

Leaves with three convergent nerves and climbing habit, see *Indian Jujube* on p. 55.

Leaves with many parallel nerves, see *Bridelia* on p. 21.

Leaves with 3–5 pairs of divergent veins, see *Flacourtia* on p. 45.

Trifoliate leaves, see *Indian Coral* on p. 53.

Digitate leaves, see *Silk Cotton* on p. 101.

SECTION III

BRANCHED TREES, UNARMED but MILKY

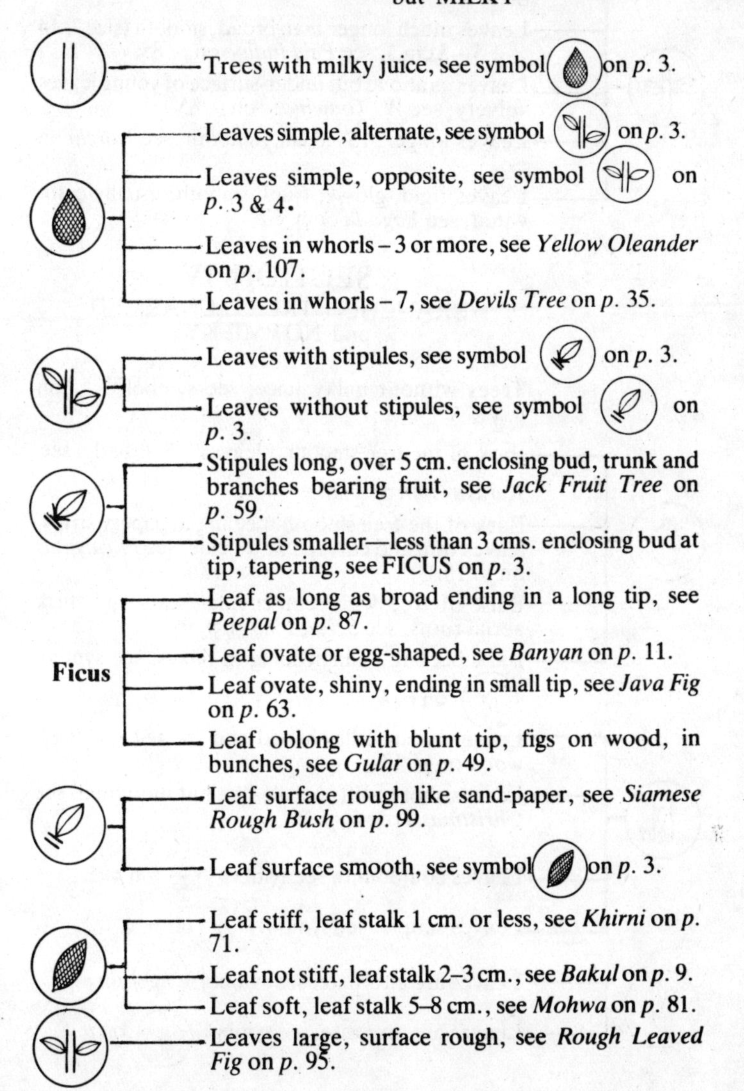

— Trees with milky juice, see symbol on p. 3.

— Leaves simple, alternate, see symbol on p. 3.
— Leaves simple, opposite, see symbol on p. 3 & 4.
— Leaves in whorls – 3 or more, see *Yellow Oleander* on p. 107.
— Leaves in whorls – 7, see *Devils Tree* on p. 35.

— Leaves with stipules, see symbol on p. 3.
— Leaves without stipules, see symbol on p. 3.

— Stipules long, over 5 cm. enclosing bud, trunk and branches bearing fruit, see *Jack Fruit Tree* on p. 59.
— Stipules smaller—less than 3 cms. enclosing bud at tip, tapering, see FICUS on p. 3.

Ficus
— Leaf as long as broad ending in a long tip, see *Peepal* on p. 87.
— Leaf ovate or egg-shaped, see *Banyan* on p. 11.
— Leaf ovate, shiny, ending in small tip, see *Java Fig* on p. 63.
— Leaf oblong with blunt tip, figs on wood, in bunches, see *Gular* on p. 49.

— Leaf surface rough like sand-paper, see *Siamese Rough Bush* on p. 99.
— Leaf surface smooth, see symbol on p. 3.

— Leaf stiff, leaf stalk 1 cm. or less, see *Khirni* on p. 71.
— Leaf not stiff, leaf stalk 2–3 cm., see *Bakul* on p. 9.
— Leaf soft, leaf stalk 5–8 cm., see *Mohwa* on p. 81.

— Leaves large, surface rough, see *Rough Leaved Fig* on p. 95.

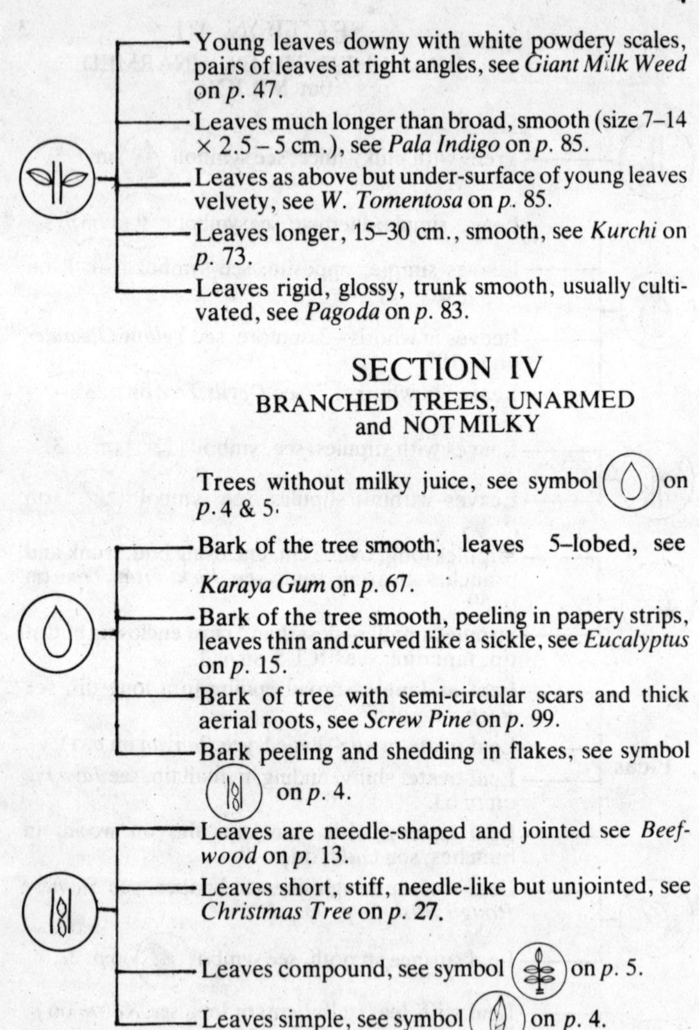

Young leaves downy with white powdery scales, pairs of leaves at right angles, see *Giant Milk Weed* on *p*. 47.

Leaves much longer than broad, smooth (size 7–14 × 2.5 – 5 cm.), see *Pala Indigo* on *p*. 85.

Leaves as above but under-surface of young leaves velvety, see *W. Tomentosa* on *p*. 85.

Leaves longer, 15–30 cm., smooth, see *Kurchi* on *p*. 73.

Leaves rigid, glossy, trunk smooth, usually cultivated, see *Pagoda* on *p*. 83.

SECTION IV

BRANCHED TREES, UNARMED and NOT MILKY

Trees without milky juice, see symbol on *p*. 4 & 5.

Bark of the tree smooth, leaves 5–lobed, see *Karaya Gum* on *p*. 67.

Bark of the tree smooth, peeling in papery strips, leaves thin and curved like a sickle, see *Eucalyptus* on *p*. 15.

Bark of tree with semi-circular scars and thick aerial roots, see *Screw Pine* on *p*. 99.

Bark peeling and shedding in flakes, see symbol on *p*. 4.

Leaves are needle-shaped and jointed see *Beefwood* on *p*. 13.

Leaves short, stiff, needle-like but unjointed, see *Christmas Tree* on *p*. 27.

Leaves compound, see symbol on *p*. 5.

Leaves simple, see symbol on *p*. 4.

Leaves are alternate, see symbol on *p*. 5.

Leaves are opposite, see symbol on *p*. 5.

5

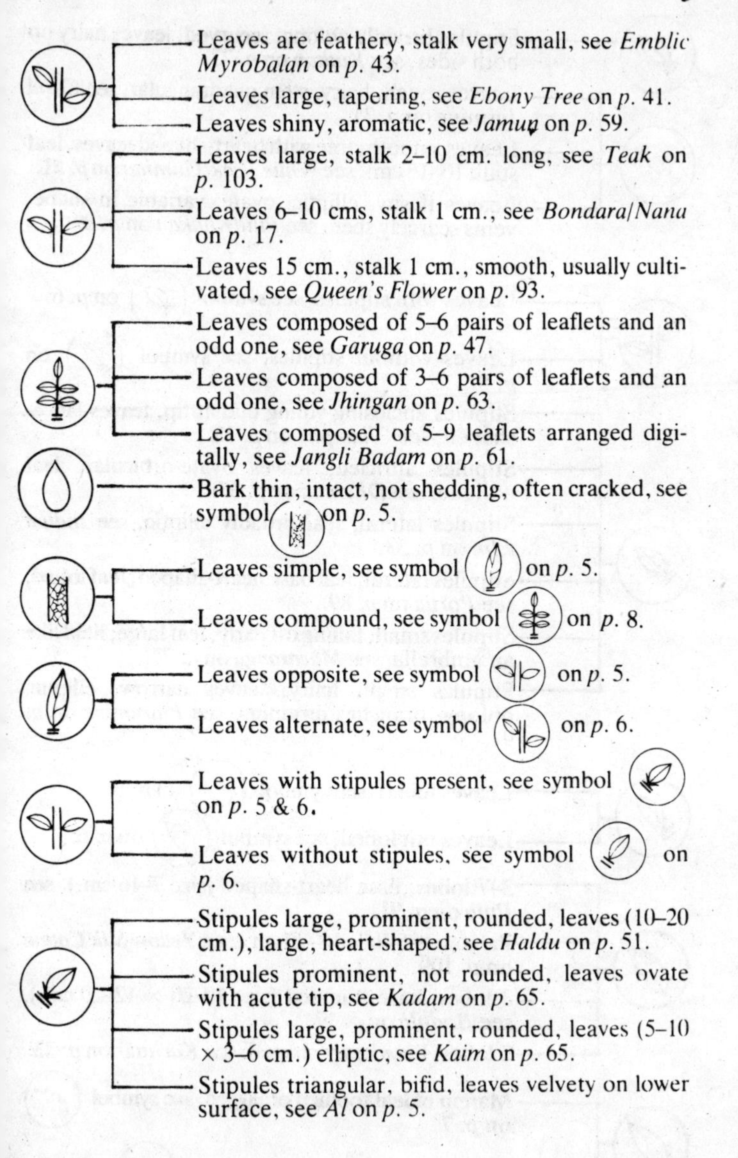

- Leaves are feathery, stalk very small, see *Emblic Myrobalan* on *p*. 43.
- Leaves large, tapering, see *Ebony Tree* on *p*. 41.
- Leaves shiny, aromatic, see *Jamun* on *p*. 59.

- Leaves large, stalk 2–10 cm. long, see *Teak* on *p*. 103.
- Leaves 6–10 cms, stalk 1 cm., see *Bondara/Nana* on *p*. 17.
- Leaves 15 cm., stalk 1 cm., smooth, usually cultivated, see *Queen's Flower* on *p*. 93.

- Leaves composed of 5–6 pairs of leaflets and an odd one, see *Garuga* on *p*. 47.
- Leaves composed of 3–6 pairs of leaflets and an odd one, see *Jhingan* on *p*. 63.
- Leaves composed of 5–9 leaflets arranged digitally, see *Jangli Badam* on *p*. 61.

- Bark thin, intact, not shedding, often cracked, see symbol on *p*. 5.

- Leaves simple, see symbol on *p*. 5.
- Leaves compound, see symbol on *p*. 8.

- Leaves opposite, see symbol on *p*. 5.
- Leaves alternate, see symbol on *p*. 6.

- Leaves with stipules present, see symbol on *p*. 5 & 6.
- Leaves without stipules, see symbol on *p*. 6.

- Stipules large, prominent, rounded, leaves (10–20 cm.), large, heart-shaped, see *Haldu* on *p*. 51.
- Stipules prominent, not rounded, leaves ovate with acute tip, see *Kadam* on *p*. 65.
- Stipules large, prominent, rounded, leaves (5–10 × 3–6 cm.) elliptic, see *Kaim* on *p*. 65.
- Stipules triangular, bifid, leaves velvety on lower surface, see *Al* on *p*. 5.

Stipules broadly oblong, recurved, leaves hairy on both sides, see *Kuthan* on *p.* 73.

Leaves rough, hairy, stem quadrangular, see *Coral Jasmine* on *p.* 31.

Leaves smooth, tree with heart-shaped leaves, leaf stalk 10–15 cm., see *White Teak/Gumhar* on *p.* 51.

Leaves fleshy, elliptic, ovate, variable in shape, veins scarcely seen, see *Pilu/Khakan* on *p.* 89.

Leaves with stipules, see symbol on *p.* 6.

Leaves without stipules, see symbol on *p.* 6.

Stipules enclosing young bud at tip, leaves lance-shaped, see *Champak* on *p.* 25.

Stipules auricled, leaves ovate-orbicular, leaf oblique, see *Dhaman* on *p.* 37.

Stipules lateral, leaf broadly elliptic, see *Indian Elm* on *p.* 53.

Stipules lateral, leaf base heart-shaped, leaf lobed, see *Portia* on *p.* 89.

Stipules small, falling off early, leaf large, held like an umbrella, see *Macaranga* on *p.* 77.

Stipules small, hairy, leaves narrow, elliptic, oblong, branches drooping, see *Putranjiva* on *p.* 91.

Leaves lobed, see symbol on *p.* 6.

Leaves not lobed, see symbol on *p.* 6.

3–7 lobes, base heart-shaped (size 7–16 cm.), see *Pula* on *p.* 91.

Palmately 5-lobed 8–20 cm., see *Yellow Silk Cotton* on *p.* 109.

3 lobes, base rounded (size 10–20 × 12–20 cm.), see *Bodula* on *p.* 17.

2 lobes, base heart-shaped, see *Kachnar* on *p.* 23.

Margin of leaf toothed or jagged, see symbol on *p.* 7.

Margin of leaf entire, see symbol on *p.* 7.

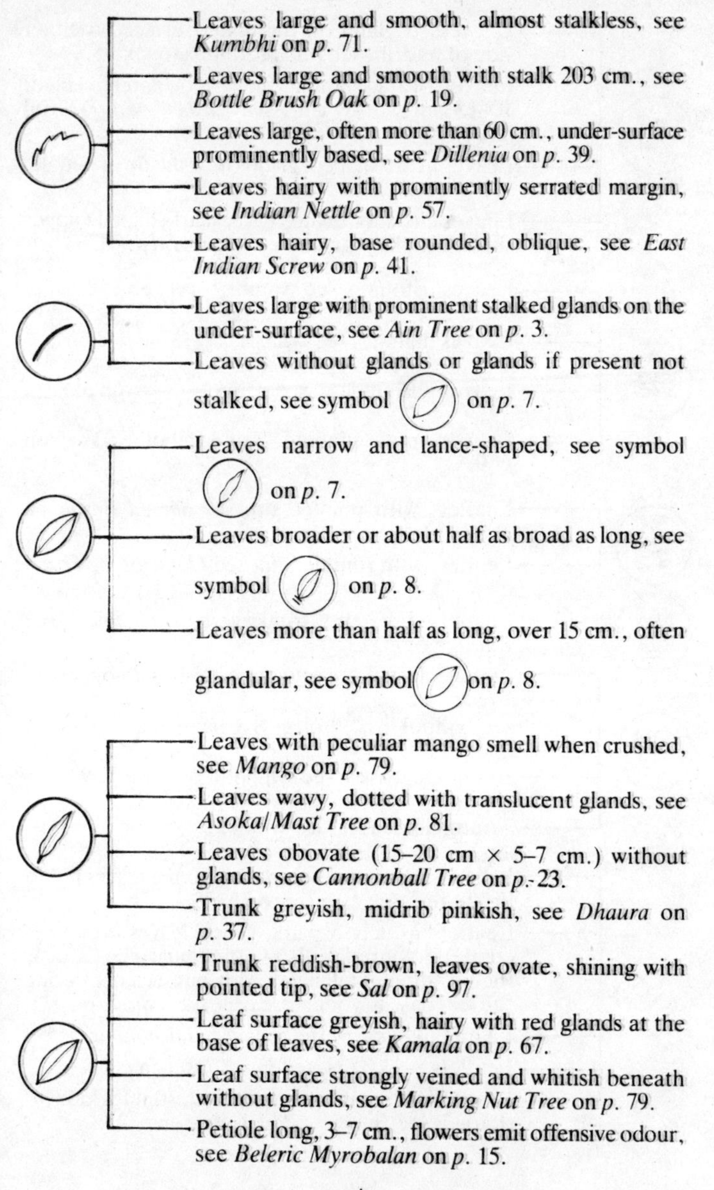

Leaves large and smooth, almost stalkless, see *Kumbhi* on *p*. 71.

Leaves large and smooth with stalk 203 cm., see *Bottle Brush Oak* on *p*. 19.

Leaves large, often more than 60 cm., under-surface prominently based, see *Dillenia* on *p*. 39.

Leaves hairy with prominently serrated margin, see *Indian Nettle* on *p*. 57.

Leaves hairy, base rounded, oblique, see *East Indian Screw* on *p*. 41.

Leaves large with prominent stalked glands on the under-surface, see *Ain Tree* on *p*. 3.

Leaves without glands or glands if present not stalked, see symbol on *p*. 7.

Leaves narrow and lance-shaped, see symbol on *p*. 7.

Leaves broader or about half as broad as long, see symbol on *p*. 8.

Leaves more than half as long, over 15 cm., often glandular, see symbol on *p*. 8.

Leaves with peculiar mango smell when crushed, see *Mango* on *p*. 79.

Leaves wavy, dotted with translucent glands, see *Asoka/Mast Tree* on *p*. 81.

Leaves obovate (15–20 cm × 5–7 cm.) without glands, see *Cannonball Tree* on *p*. 23.

Trunk greyish, midrib pinkish, see *Dhaura* on *p*. 37.

Trunk reddish-brown, leaves ovate, shining with pointed tip, see *Sal* on *p*. 97.

Leaf surface greyish, hairy with red glands at the base of leaves, see *Kamala* on *p*. 67.

Leaf surface strongly veined and whitish beneath without glands, see *Marking Nut Tree* on *p*. 79.

Petiole long, 3–7 cm., flowers emit offensive odour, see *Beleric Myrobalan* on *p*. 15.

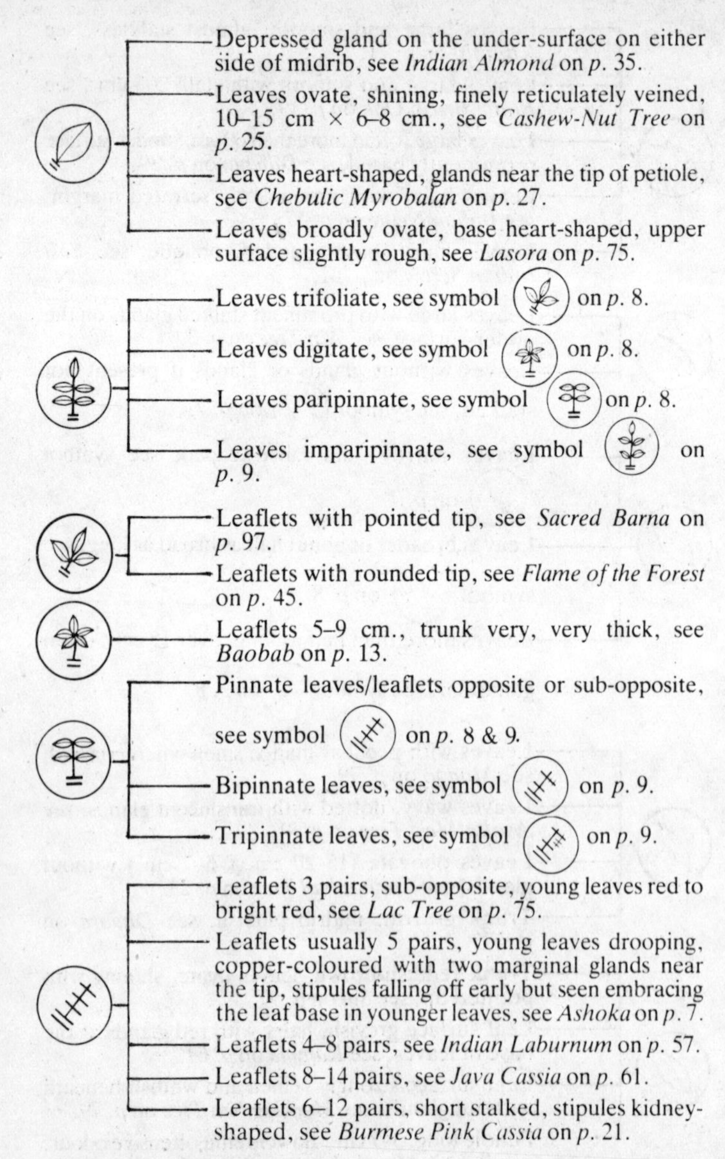

Depressed gland on the under-surface on either side of midrib, see *Indian Almond* on *p.* 35.

Leaves ovate, shining, finely reticulately veined, 10–15 cm × 6–8 cm., see *Cashew-Nut Tree* on *p.* 25.

Leaves heart-shaped, glands near the tip of petiole, see *Chebulic Myrobalan* on *p.* 27.

Leaves broadly ovate, base heart-shaped, upper surface slightly rough, see *Lasora* on *p.* 75.

Leaves trifoliate, see symbol on *p.* 8.

Leaves digitate, see symbol on *p.* 8.

Leaves paripinnate, see symbol on *p.* 8.

Leaves imparipinnate, see symbol on *p.* 9.

Leaflets with pointed tip, see *Sacred Barna* on *p.* 97.

Leaflets with rounded tip, see *Flame of the Forest* on *p.* 45.

Leaflets 5–9 cm., trunk very, very thick, see *Baobab* on *p.* 13.

Pinnate leaves/leaflets opposite or sub-opposite, see symbol on *p.* 8 & 9.

Bipinnate leaves, see symbol on *p.* 9.

Tripinnate leaves, see symbol on *p.* 9.

Leaflets 3 pairs, sub-opposite, young leaves red to bright red, see *Lac Tree* on *p.* 75.

Leaflets usually 5 pairs, young leaves drooping, copper-coloured with two marginal glands near the tip, stipules falling off early but seen embracing the leaf base in younger leaves, see *Ashoka* on *p.* 7.

Leaflets 4–8 pairs, see *Indian Laburnum* on *p.* 57.

Leaflets 8–14 pairs, see *Java Cassia* on *p.* 61.

Leaflets 6–12 pairs, short stalked, stipules kidney-shaped, see *Burmese Pink Cassia* on *p.* 21.

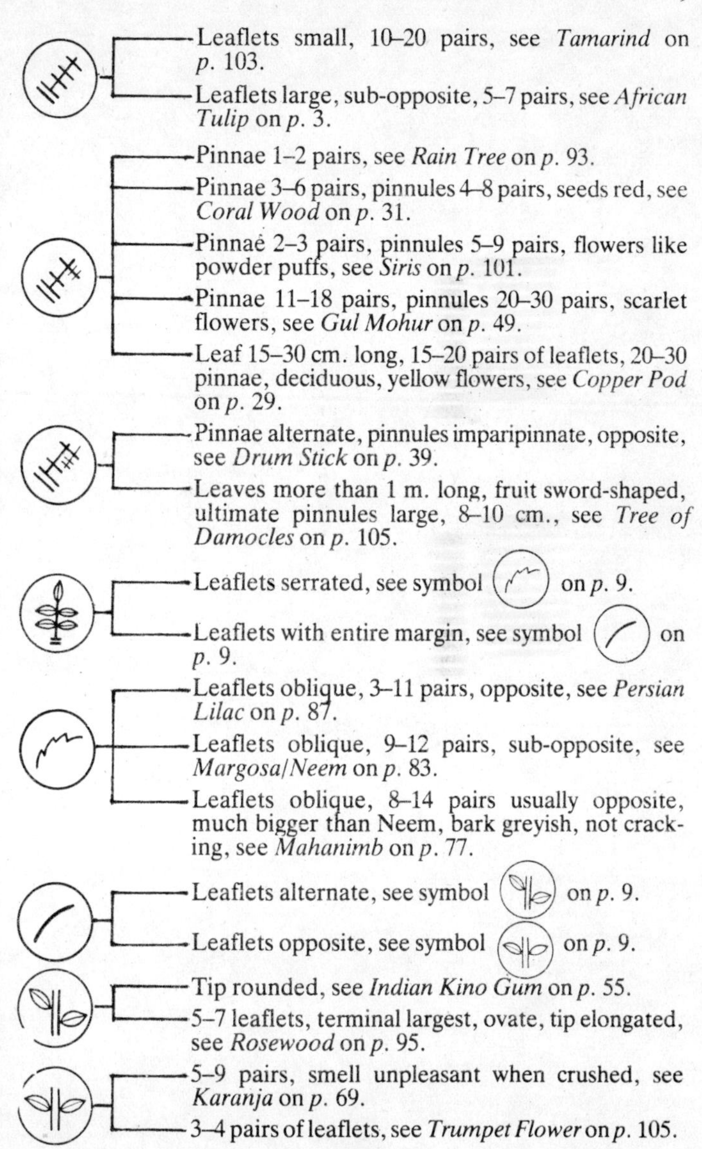

Leaflets small, 10–20 pairs, see *Tamarind* on *p*. 103.

Leaflets large, sub-opposite, 5–7 pairs, see *African Tulip* on *p*. 3.

Pinnae 1–2 pairs, see *Rain Tree* on *p*. 93.

Pinnae 3–6 pairs, pinnules 4–8 pairs, seeds red, see *Coral Wood* on *p*. 31.

Pinnae 2–3 pairs, pinnules 5–9 pairs, flowers like powder puffs, see *Siris* on *p*. 101.

Pinnae 11–18 pairs, pinnules 20–30 pairs, scarlet flowers, see *Gul Mohur* on *p*. 49.

Leaf 15–30 cm. long, 15–20 pairs of leaflets, 20–30 pinnae, deciduous, yellow flowers, see *Copper Pod* on *p*. 29.

Pinnae alternate, pinnules imparipinnate, opposite, see *Drum Stick* on *p*. 39.

Leaves more than 1 m. long, fruit sword-shaped, ultimate pinnules large, 8–10 cm., see *Tree of Damocles* on *p*. 105.

Leaflets serrated, see symbol on *p*. 9.

Leaflets with entire margin, see symbol on *p*. 9.

Leaflets oblique, 3–11 pairs, opposite, see *Persian Lilac* on *p*. 87.

Leaflets oblique, 9–12 pairs, sub-opposite, see *Margosa/Neem* on *p*. 83.

Leaflets oblique, 8–14 pairs usually opposite, much bigger than Neem, bark greyish, not cracking, see *Mahanimb* on *p*. 77.

Leaflets alternate, see symbol on *p*. 9.

Leaflets opposite, see symbol on *p*. 9.

Tip rounded, see *Indian Kino Gum* on *p*. 55.

5–7 leaflets, terminal largest, ovate, tip elongated, see *Rosewood* on *p*. 95.

5–9 pairs, smell unpleasant when crushed, see *Karanja* on *p*. 69.

3–4 pairs of leaflets, see *Trumpet Flower* on *p*. 105.

DESCRIPTION AND ILLUSTRATIONS

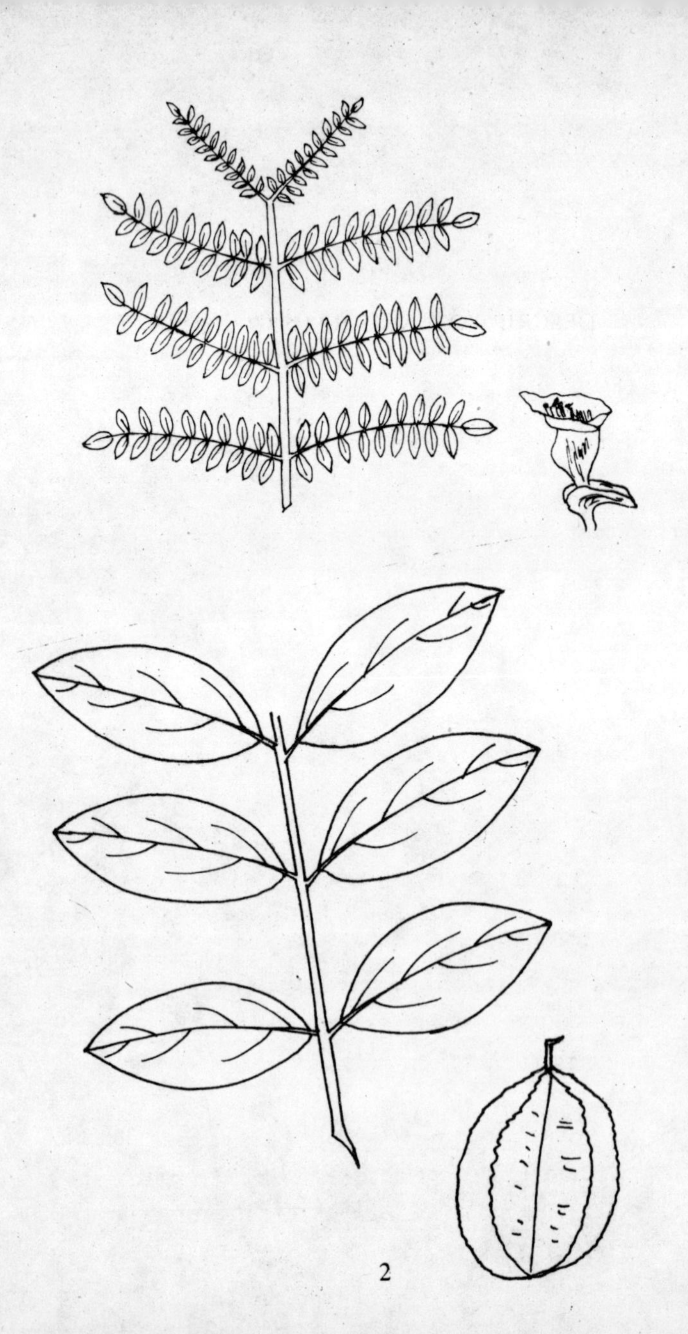

2

AFRICAN TULIP (TREE)

Spathodea campanulata Beaub. *Bignoniaceae*

A fairly tall, evergreen tree upto 25–30m. high with light-grey, fibrous bark. Rather short branches giving the tree a somewhat slender outline.

LEAVES : Compound, opposite, divided into an odd number of pointed leaflets (9–19 pairs + 1), ovate, lance-shaped, entire, long pointed 5–10 – 4–8 cm.

FLOWERS : In cold season (Nov.–Dec.), the velvety brown buds appear in cone-like masses at the ends of branches and soon they burst forth into large clusters of bloom—scarlet-red in colour—with wide bell-shaped flowers. Much nectar is stored in the base of the flowers which attract a large number of birds and bats. Most pollination seems to be effected by birds.

FRUIT : Long, pointed, woody pod containing many winged seeds.

The tree is a native of central Africa and introduced as a decorative tree due to its evergreen foliage and showy flowers. Suitable as an avenue tree in the tropics, it is cultivated on roadsides, in parks and gardens in the plains.

AIN/ASAN

Terminalia alata Heyne ex Roth *Combretaceae*
(= *T. crenulata* W. & A.
= *T. tomentosa* W. & A.)

Ain (Mar./Beng.), Asan (Hindi), Karamarda (Tam.), Saadar (Guj.). Saj (Hindi), Tani (Tel.)

A small, ungainly tree, upto 10–15m. high, trunk more or less straight with rough grey bark deeply cracked, young parts more or less clothed with yellowish brown pubescence.

LEAVES : Sub-opposite, uppermost often alternate, rough, 8–12 × 5–8cm. ovate-oblong, 3–4 times longer than broad. Softly hairy when young, smooth to touch when old, 1 or 2 top-shaped glands near midrib on the lower side, base often heart-shaped.

FLOWERS : Dull yellow, small, in pubescent spikes, April–June.

FRUIT : 3–5cm. with 5 fibrous, stiff wings.

Common throughout deciduous forests, all over India. 3 varieties are recognized. Timber useful.

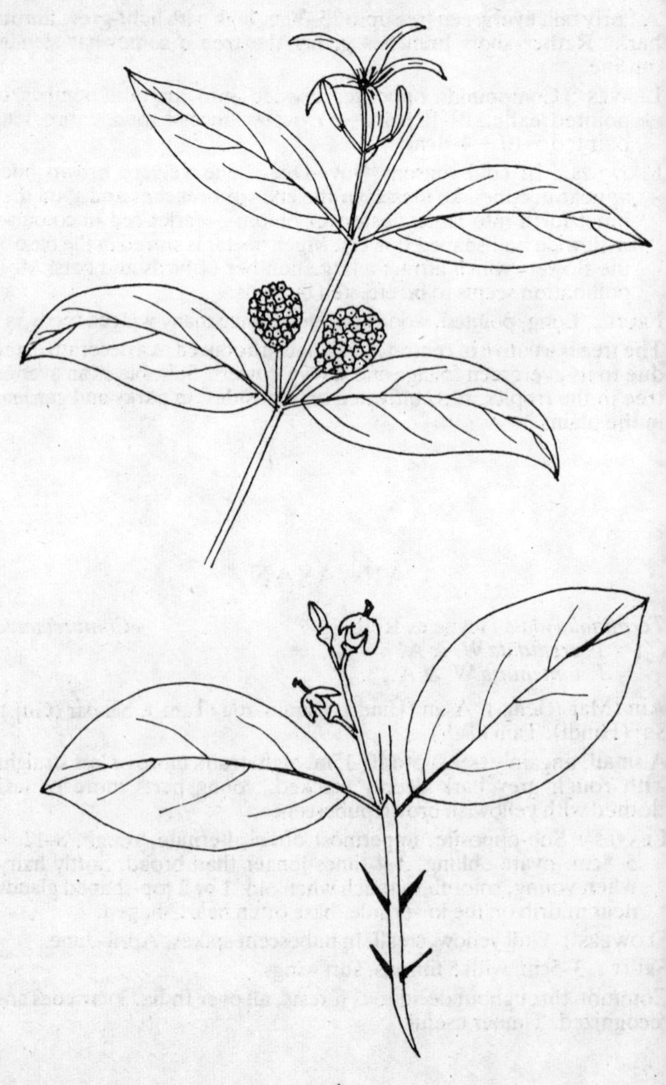

AL

Morinda coreia Buch-Ham *Rubiaceae*
= *M. tinctoria* Roxb.

Ach, Al. (Hindi/Beng.), Barachand (Beng.), Bartondi (Mar.), Haldi Kunch (Beng.)

Shrub or small tree upto 8m. high, young branches 4-angled, hairy.

LEAVES : Broadly elliptic, bright green, shiny, hairy on both sides, 10–15 × 5–8cm., pointed tip, stipules bifid.

FLOWERS : Pure white in ball-like clusters, throughout the year.

FRUIT : Globose, ellipsoid, 2cm. or more in diam.; appears to have 12 polygonal faces, hence the vernacular name. White when ripe.

Common in lower hills in W. India. Roots yield a red dye.

ALU

Meyna laxiflora Robyns *Rubiaceae*
(= *Vangueria spinosa* Hook.)

Alu (Guj./Mar.), Muyna, Muduna (Hindi), Mullakare (Kan.), Veliki (Tam.), Vasikilammu (Tel.)

A small evergreen tree upto 10m. high, trunk almost smooth with dark brown bark with straight spines.

LEAVES : Opposite, elliptic, 5–13 × 2–7cm., highly polished with 6–9 pairs of side veins. Stipules triangular.

FLOWERS : Greenish-white, hairy within, arising in flat-topped clusters, Jan.–Apr.

FRUIT : Yellowish, round, 4–5cm., sweet, edible. Fermenting when ripe.

Common in plains and low hills in deciduous forests.

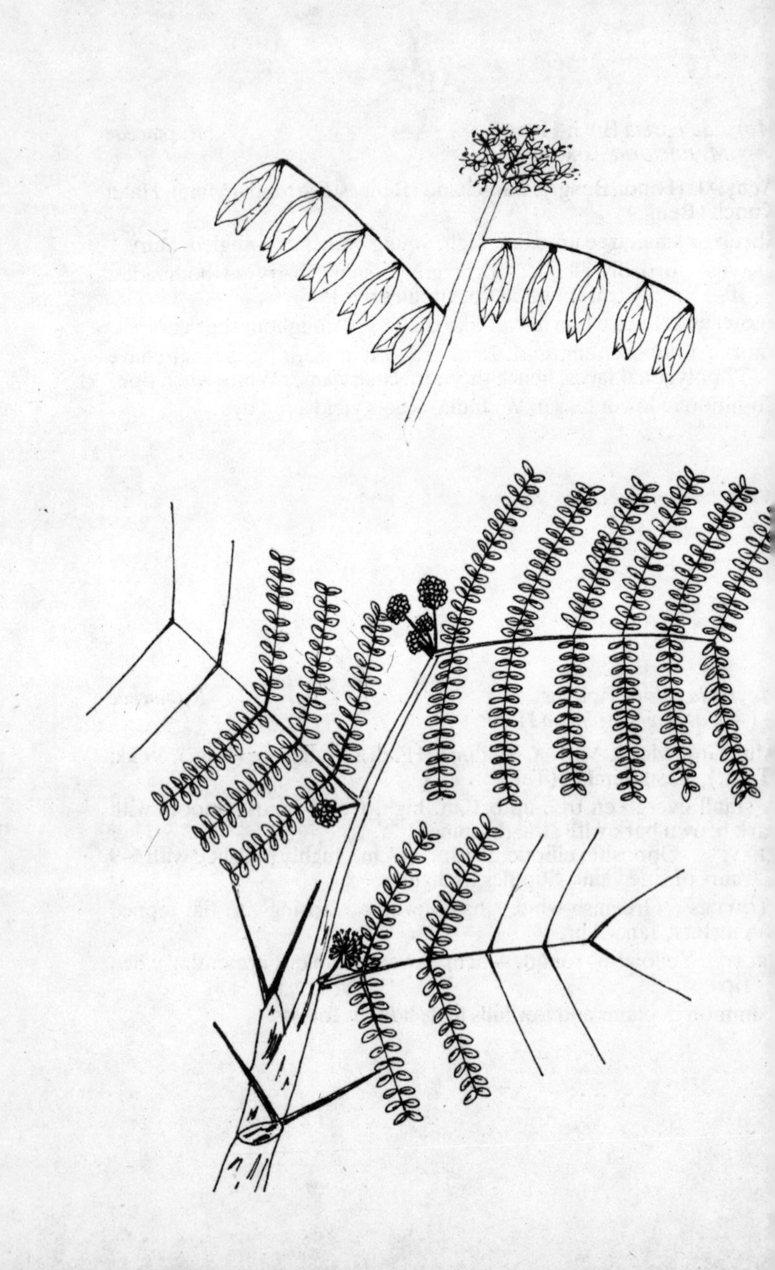

ASHOKA TREE

Saraca asoca (Roxb.) De Wilde *Caesalpinaceae*
(= *S. indica* L.)

Asogam (Tam.); Ashoka (Hindi, Beng., Mar., Guj.); Asokam (Mal.)

A medium-sized evergreen tree upto 10m. with bark varying from dark brown to almost black. Trunk has a warty surface.

LEAVES : Paripinnate with 3–6 pairs of leaflets. Each leaflet oblong-lanceolate 10–20 × 2–3cm., gracefully pendant and copper-coloured when young with marginal glands near the apex.

FLOWERS : Orange to orange-yellow turning red in dense heads, often arising on the branches from the wood.

FRUITS : Flat pods 10–20 × 3–5cm., leathery with 2–5 compressed seeds.

Usually found alongside streams or in the shade of evergreen forests. 'The vegetable world scarce exhibits a richer sight than the Ashoka tree in full bloom.' (Sir Wm. Jones).[1] One of the trees held most sacred by Hindus and Buddhists. It is propagated through seeds and is frequently cultivated as an ornamental throughout the tropics.

BABUL

Acacia nilotica (Linn.) Del Mimosaceae
(= *A. arabica* Lamk.)

Babul (Beng./Hindi/Mar.), Baval (Guj.), Karuvelam (Mal.), Karuveli (Tam.), Kikar (Punj.), Nallatumma (Tel.)

Small, evergreen tree, upto 7m. high, dark-brown trunk with longitudinally fissured bark.

LEAVES : Twice divided. (Bipinnate), 4–13cm., 2–6 pairs of leaflets with 10–20 pairs of pinnules. Two cup-shaped glands usually present on the leaf-stalk. A pair of grey-white spines, 1½–5cm., in the axil.

FLOWERS : Minute in golden-yellow globular clusters, fragrant, Jul.–Dec.

FRUIT : Flat pod, covered with soft whitish hair, upto 10–12cm; constricted between seeds (6–10).

Common in drier parts of the plains. Can stand water-logging for long period. Wood hard; yields acacia-type of gum.

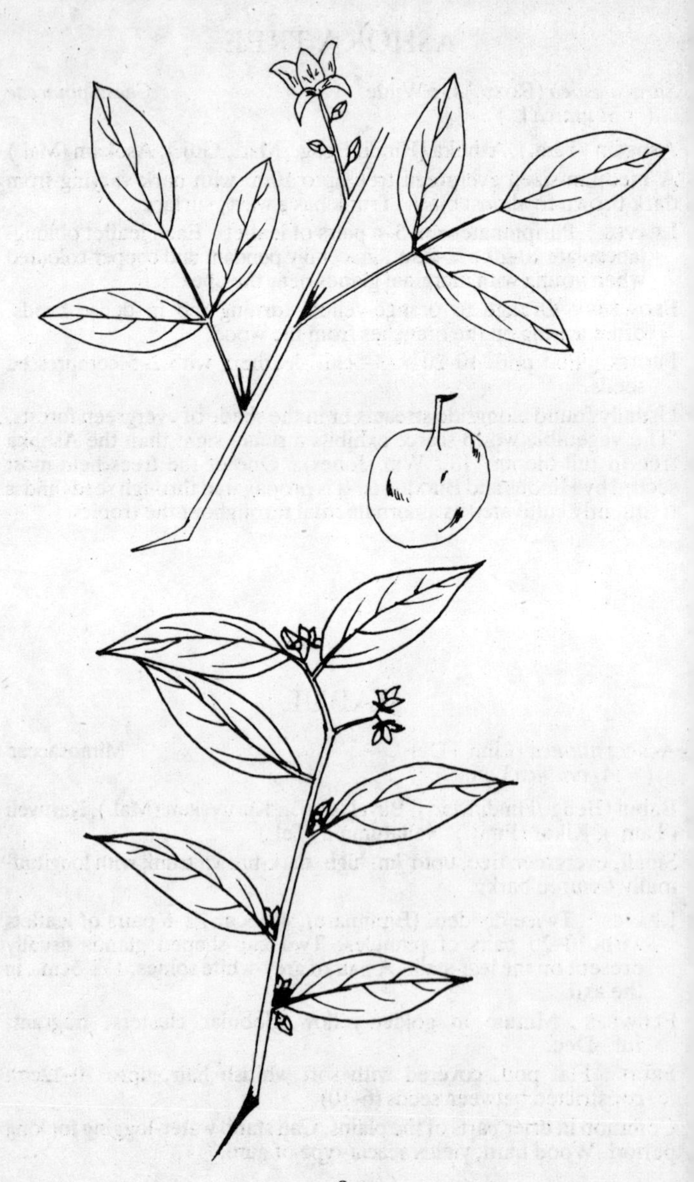

BAEL

Aegle marmelos Corr. *Rutaceae*

Bael (Beng./Hindi./Mar.), Bili (Guj.), Muredu (Tel.) Vilvan (Tam./Mal.)

Middle-sized, evergreen tree, upto 10m. high, thorny, with rough greyish bark.

LEAVES : 3-foliate, each leaflet smooth, lance-shaped 3–8 × 1½–4cm, lateral or side leaflets without stalk, terminal one with stalk, 2–3cm.

FLOWERS : Small, greenish-white, sweet-scented, April–May.

FRUIT : Greyish-yellow, spherical with a hard-shell, 5–13cm. in diam., pulp sweet-sour; edible, used as a refreshing drink in summer. Seeds many.

Cultivated throughout India in plains, particularly near Shiva temples. Also wild in deciduous forests. Do not thrive at all on hills above 1000m.

BAKUL/MAULSARI

Mimusops elengi Linn. *Sapotaceae*

Bakul (Beng./Kan.), Borsali (Guj.), Elengi (Mal.), Maulsari (Hindi). Pogada (Tel.), Vagulam (Tam.)

A graceful evergreen tree upto 15m. high, trunk more or less smooth with scaly bark. Crown compact and leafy. Trunk and branches often infected by a stem borer, showering wood-dust on the ground.

LEAVES : 6–10 × 3–5cm. elliptic, tip elongated (acuminate), smooth.

FLOWERS : Whitish, fragrant, nearly 1–1½cm. across, solitary or in clusters, Jan–March.

FRUIT : A berry, ovoid about 2cm. long, yellow-red when ripe, 1–2 seeded.

Frequently occurring in deciduous forests, often cultivated for its fragrant flowers and evergreen crown. Can stand pruning and used as a cupola tree in Mughal gardens.

BAMBOO

Poaceae
Graminae

Bans (Hindi/Beng.), Mungil (Tam./Mal.), Vans (Guj./Mar.)

Not strictly speaking trees, bamboos look like and grow to the size of trees. Actually they are perennial tall grasses with woody stems.

The bamboo cane grows in joints, either straight, unbranched or branching from 10–15cm. upto 40cm. They arise from an underground root-stock, often forming a large dense mass.

LEAVES : Variable in size, have a lower part (stalk) that embraces the stem at a joint bearing a blade.

FLOWERS : Small in clusters, rather rare. Flowering of bamboo takes place after a certain number of years of vegetative growth. After the flowering is over the clump usually dies.

FRUIT : Rather rare, ranging from the size of wheat grain chaff to the size of a fist. It is said that the population of jungle mice grows too rapidly when bamboos flower and fruit. The rapid regeneration of bamboo from seed is proverbial.

Several types of bamboos occur in India. *Bambusa arundinacea* and *Dendrocalamus strictus* are common in our forests in the plains. They are cultivated also by the paper industry and serve a large number of human needs.

BANYAN

Ficus bengalensis Linn. *Moraceae*

Ala, Alam (Kan./Mal./Tam.) Bar, Bargad (Hindi), Bat (Beng.), Marri (Tel.) Vad(Guj./Mar.)

A huge spreading tree with a large number of hanging or column-like roots, which extend the growth of the tree indefinitely (upto 20m. tall). Branches and trunk smooth, milky.

LEAVES : Ovate, smooth, shining, deep green above, paler green, pubescent below. Bud covered by a conical stipule.

FLOWERS : Inconspicuous, inside the figs which grow between the upper part of the leaf-stalk and the stem. March–April.

FRUIT : The fig turns red and become soft on maturity. The tree looks very elegant when the branches are studded with ripe fruits, and is visited by numerous birds chirping happily throughout the day.

This is also a sacred tree to the Hindus. Generally planted all over the plains of India; wild only in the sub-Himalayan forests. It is a great boon to the weary traveller during the summer heat for shade.

'So like the temple did it seem that there a pious heart's first impulse would be prayer' (Southey).[2]

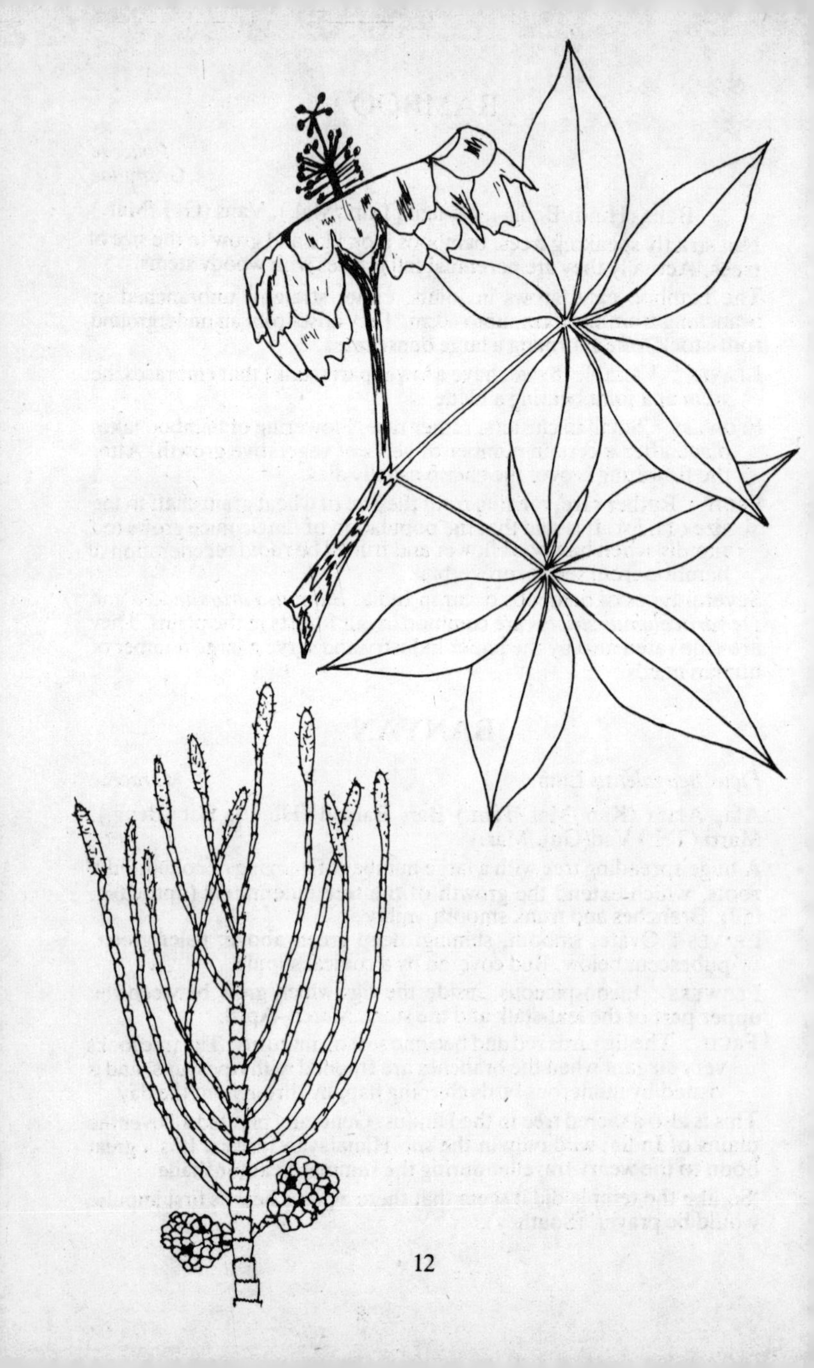

BAOBAB

Adansonia digitata Linn. *Bombacaceae*

Anaipuli (Tam.), Gorakh Amli (Hindi/Guj.). Gorakh chinch(Mar.)

The stoutest deciduous tree that is considered long-living. The trunk is grotesquely fat, suddenly tapering into branches. Bark smooth, greyish.

LEAVES : Alternate, palmately compound, digitate. Each leaflet lance-shaped, about 8–12 × 4–6cm., light green, smooth.

FLOWERS : Large, white, about 15cm. across when open. Stamens purplish gathered into a large bundle. Blooms generally appear when the tree is leafless.

FRUIT : Oval 20–30cm. long, greyish, gourd-shaped, hanging from a thick stalk. Pulp relished by monkeys.

A native of tropical Africa in the Lion region. Found scattered, particularly on the western coast. In Africa it is said to have attained an age of 5000 years (Ida Colthurst quoting Adamson).[3]

BEEFWOOD

Casuarina equisetifolia Linn. Casuarinaceae

Chavukku (Mal./Kan./Tel.), Jangli Saru (Hindi), Jhau (Beng.), Sarugudu (Tel.), Savukku (Tam.), Suru (Mar.), Vilayti Saru (Guj.)

A tall, straight, erect tree upto 30m. high, outwardly resembling a pine tree (saru). Numerous drooping branches with 6–8 angled needles looking like leaves. Bark rough, brown, exfoliating in longitudinal strips.

LEAVES : The needles, which are actually joined stems, are covered by triangular scale-like leaves at the joints.

FLOWERS : Unisexual; male in small spikes and female in roundish clusters may appear on the same or separate trees. Feb.–Apr. and Sept.–Oct.

FRUIT : Brownish, globose, woody cones 1.5–2cm., containing tiny winged 'seeds'.

Wild near Bengal coast, but commonly cultivated on roadsides and in gardens all over the plains. Thrives best in coastal regions. The branches when swayed by wind create a sound on beaches which is pleasant to the ear.

BELLERIC MYROBALAN

Terminala bellerica Roxb. *Combretaceae*

Bahera (Hindi/Guj.), Beheda (Mar.), Bohera (Beng.), Tani (Tel./Tam.), Thani (Mal.)

A large handsome deciduous tree upto 20m. high with buttresses at the base.

LEAVES : Clustered at the ends of branches, leathery, elliptic-oblong, tapering at the base into a long petiole, 10–15 × 8–10cm. The leaves turn red before falling. Glands may or may not be present near midrib beneath.

FLOWERS : Yellowish in axillary spikes, emit a sickly smell. Feb.–May.

FRUIT : A globose woody drupe about 2–3cm. covered with brownish velvety hair.

Common in deciduous mixed forests throughout India. Yields belleric myrobalans for commercial astringent, used for tanning and in indigenous medicine.

BLUE GUM TREE / EUCALYPTUS

Eucalyptus species *Myrtaceae*

Nilgiri tree (Hindi/Guj./Mar./Tam.)

Evergreen aromatic trees indigenous to Australia. The tallest trees of the genus are known to exceed 100m. in height. Various species and their hybrids are cultivated for their oil (from leaves) and wood.

Tall and slender trees, sparsely clothed and characteristic leaves with smooth brownish peeling bark or greyish non-peeling type of bark.

LEAVES : Simple, sickle-shaped (curved) in a lateral plane, 10–15cm., generally smooth but may be velvet in young stages. They lend a characteristic appearance to the tree by their dull green colour, lateral position and drooping habit.

FLOWERS : In drooping clusters of 6–12 flowers from the ends of branches.

FRUITS : Conical with a flat top (obconical), varying in size from 1–2cm. in diam.

Eucalyptus species are remarkable for their rapid growth and selected hybrids are increasingly being cultivated for their wood which can be used as poles, construction timber, firewood and for paper pulp. Some species yield a valuable essential oil that is used by cosmetic and pharmaceutical industries. If planted in groups, they give a point to the landscape.

E. robusta, E. citriorora, E. globulus are the commoner species. The latter two prefer well drained soils and are grown in the temperate regions of the Nilgiri hills for production of volatile (essential) oil.

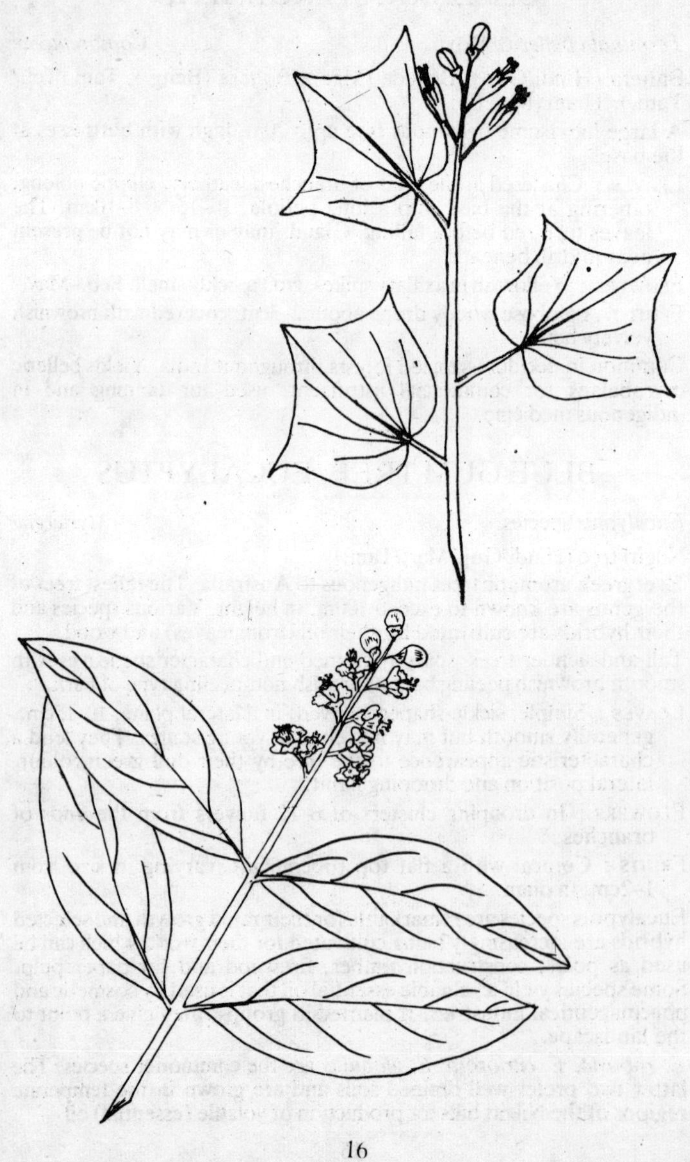

BODULA

rythropsis colorata (Roxb.) Burkill *Sterculiaceae*
(= *Firmiana colorata* R. Br.
= *Sterculia colorata* Roxb.)

odula (Hindi), Karaka (Tel.), Kaushi (Mar.), Malam herutti (Tam.), lalam paratthi (Mal.), Mula (Beng.)

straight, medium-sized deciduous tree upto 10m. high. Trunk raight, covered with thick, scaly ash-coloured bark and a crown of reading branches.

EAVES : Crowded at the ends of branches on slender stalks; 10–20cm. × 8.30cm., 3–5 pointed shallow lobes. Young leaves and shoots downy. Leaves are shed from Jan. to April.

.OWERS : Bright coral-orange red when the tree is leafless, make the tree very prominent in leafless jungle. Stalks of flowers and the tubular flowers are covered by downy hair giving the flower bunch a velvety appearance. April–May.

UITS : May be mistaken for an orange-coloured leaf bearing one or two seeds of the size of a bean on its margin.

ommon in deciduous forests of the plains.

BONDARA/NANA

gerstroemia lanceolata Wall. *Lythraceae*

ndare, Nana (Mar.), Vellilavu (Mal.), Ventaka (Tel.), Vevala m.)

middle-sized tree upto 10–15m. high, trunk smooth with ash-oured bark, peeling in longitudinal strips.

VES : Simple, opposite, lanceolate 6–10cm. × 2–5cm. Smooth above, hairy below with 8–12 pairs of prominent side veins.

WERS : Whitish, in large pyramidal clusters. Mar.–Apr.

ITS : Brownish, ellipsoid capsules 1–2cm.

elegant tree when covered with flowers, common in lower hills deciduous forests in plains.

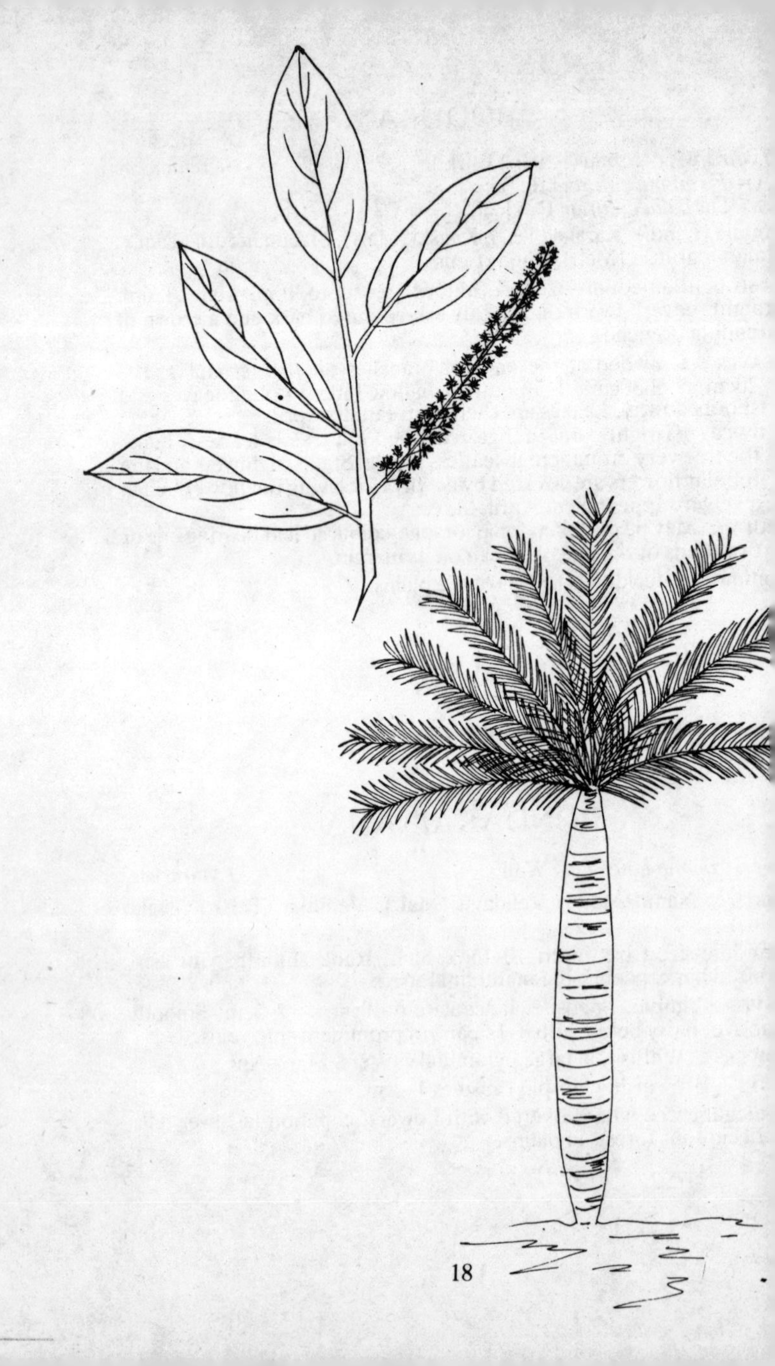

BOTTLE-BRUSH OAK

Barringtonia racemosa Roxb. *Combretaceae*

Ijjal (Hindi), Samudraphala (Hindi/Guj./Mar./Beng./S. India)

A tree of the sea-shore, capable of resisting strong sea-breeze. Evergreen, reaching upto 15m. high, very graceful with dense crown of foliage and white flowers. Bark smooth, pinkish-grey.

LEAVES : Large, obovate, blunt, leathery, 15–20 × 10–12cm. with pinkish veins, olive green, turning pink before withering, stalkless.

FLOWERS : Very large, white, 15cm. across, forming a bottle-brush of stamens with a pinkish tinge. April–May.

FRUITS : Quadrangular, urn-shaped upto 10cm. wide, broad base with tapering tip and persistent calyx, hanging down with fibrous husk.

Often cultivated at the sea-side but not on sandy beaches.

BOTTLE PALM/ROYAL PALM

Roystonea regia C.F. Cook *Arecaceae*
(= *Oreodoxa regia Kunth.*)

One of the stateliest of all palms, reaching upto 20m. in height and about 0.5–0.6m. in diam. at the base, somewhat thickened towards the upper-middle part, giving the tree a bottle-shaped appearance. Trunk smooth, light-grey with ring-like markings.

LEAVES : Feathery 2–4m. long, similar to those of the coconut palm, but the basal sheath is tubular and much larger, fully embracing the trunk below the crown.

FLOWERS : In 3–4 clusters, enclosed by two boat-shaped spathes, whitish. Male longer than female.

FRUIT : Spherical to egg-shaped, about 1–14 cm.

Native of the West Indies, commonly planted in parks and gardens; particularly suitable for graceful avenues.

BRIDELIA

Bridelia retusa Spr. *Euphorbiaceae*

Asana (Mar.), Ekdania (Hindi), Goje (Kan.), Grio (Beng.), Monj (Guj.), Nurrayini (Mal.)

A medium-sized, deciduous tree upto 10m. high, with greyish bark, spinous when young.

LEAVES : Alternate, leathery, ovate 7–15 × 3–6cm., bright green, turning pinkish before falling, slightly hairy beneath, 15–20 pairs of almost parallel side veins. Stipules ovate, unequal at base, falling off early.

FLOWERS : Greenish yellow, in crowded clusters, May.–Oct.

FRUITS : Purplish-black, globular, pea-sized.

Common on low hills (*ghats*).

BURMESE PINK CASSIA

Cassia renigera Wall. *Caesalpinaceae*

Small to medium-sized, deciduous tree, upto 6–9m. high, trunk short with a few upright branches bearing numerous drooping branchlets. Bark brownish-grey covered with small corky excrescences.

LEAVES: Feathery, drooping 10–30 cm. long, each composed of 8–12 pairs of short-stalked leaflets, downy, soft to touch. Leaf fall Dec.–March. New leaves appear in May.

FLOWERS : Rich pink and more showy than other pink Cassias. Fade to white. Arising in clusters on deep red stalks, scented. Calyx densely pubescent. Flowering period short. April–May.

FRUIT : Similar to Indian laburnum, smooth, cylindrical, 30–60cm. in length.

Native of interior Burma. Often planted in Indian gardens and on oadsides.

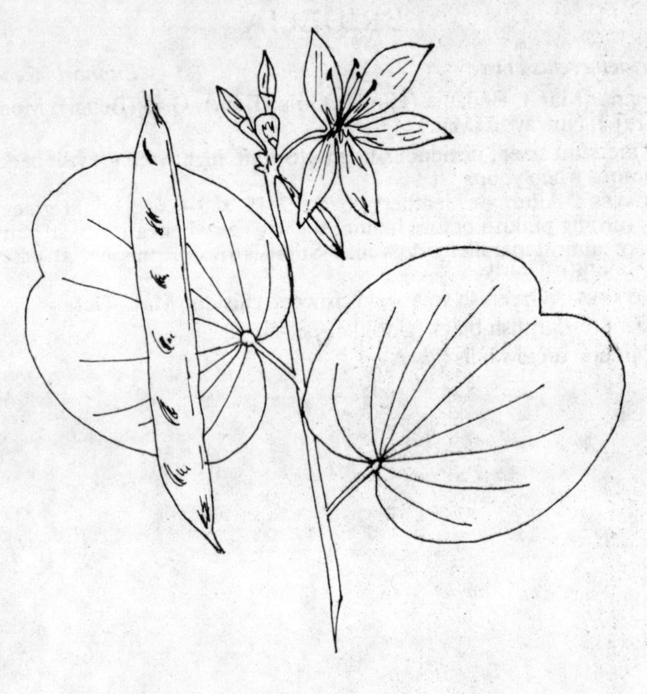

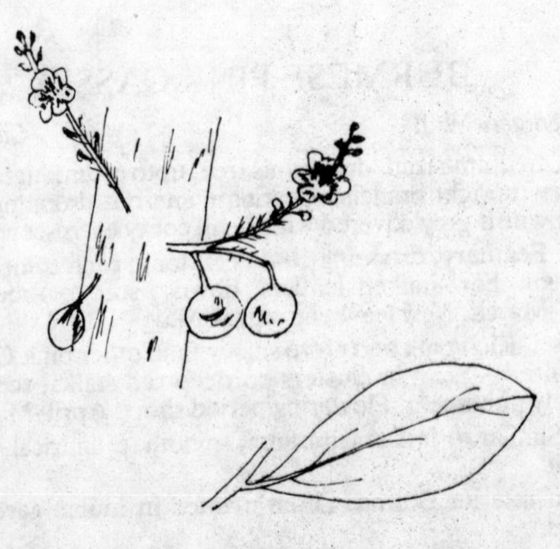

CAMEL HOOF TREE/KACHNAR/ MOUNTAIN EBONY

auhhinia purpurea Linn. *Caesalpinaceae*

ev kanchan (Beng.), Kachnar (Hindi/Guj./Mar.), Kanchanam 'el.), Mandari (Tam.)

[edium-sized, deciduous tree with crooked branches upto 7m. in ›ight.

haracteristically two-lobed, appearing like twin leaves on a stalk, about 7–10 cm. in diameter divided into 2 equal lobes.

LOWERS : Large, about 6cm. across in various tones of pink and purple, in a few flowered clusters at the ends of branches. They appear when leaves have fallen off in Mar.–April.

RUIT : Pods, 10–15cm. long, flat with 5–6 seeds.

ardy trees, usually cultivated in gardens and on roadsides.

here are several other species with smaller leaves and white to pink owers — *B. varieagata* and *B. racemosa* — occurring commonly in eciduous forests. One of the sacred trees of India.

CANNONBALL TREE

ouroupita guianensis Aubl. *Lecythidaceae*

ailaspati (Hindi/Mar.), Nagalingam (Tam.)

tall deciduous soft-wooded, erect tree upto 20m. high, with a large reading crown and dark brown trunk.

EAVES : Simple, alternate, obovate, 15–20 × 5–7cm., falling off once or twice during the year making the tree completely bare within a week. The new leaves are light green, pleasing to the eye, and reappear soon after the fall.

LOWERS : Borne on long woody racemes measuring 15–30cm. springing from the main trunk and main branches. They are curiously shaped, giving the impression of the phallic form of 'Shivalingam' covered by the snake's hood, which is formed of fused stamens surrounded by the fleshy pink petals and sepals.

RUIT : Of the size of cannon balls, globular greenish-brown. They emit an unpleasant smell when ripe.

is a native of tropical America and the W. Indies, often planted in arks, gardens and on roadsides.

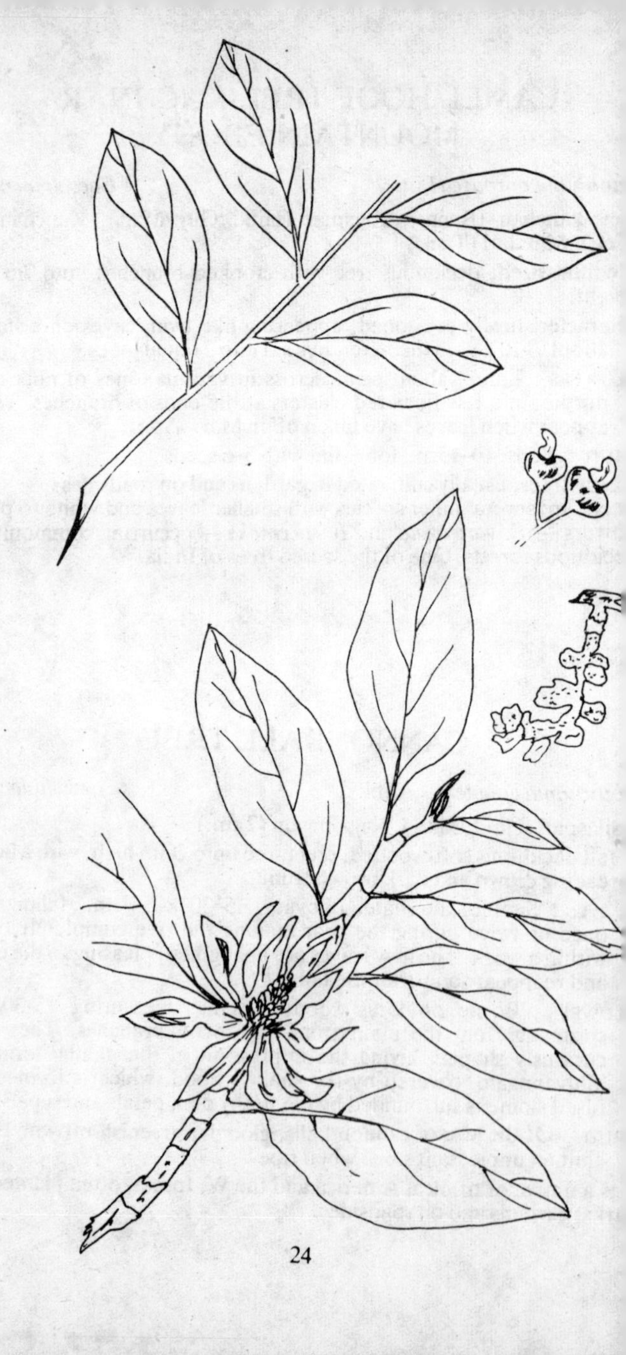

CASHEW-NUT TREE

Anacardium occidentale Linn. *Anacardiaceae*

Andiparuppu (Mal.), Hijli Badam (Beng.), Kaju (Guj./Hindi/Mar.), Muntha-mamidi (Tam.)

A widely spreading evergreen tree, growing upto 12m. high with a rough bark.

LEAVES : Alternate, ovate or obovate, 10–15 × 6–8cm. long, finely reticulately veined on a stalk 1–2 cm. in length. Shining leaves makes it an attractive tree even without flowers.

FLOWERS : Small, frequently rose-coloured, borne in panicles longer than the leaves.

FRUIT : 'An apple with a nut below' (hanging) 'is one of the curiosities of vegetable kingdom' (Nairne).[4] The apple, though tempting to the eye, is unpleasant to the normal palate, though it is edible. This is the swollen stalk of the fruit which bears the true fruit in the form of the hard-shelled nut. The nut after shelling exposes the cashew which is highly prized as dry fruit, almost like the almond. The cashew apple when fermented gives a well known liquor called 'Fenie' in Goa. The shell of the nut contains an acrid juice which causes blisters but is also used in the plastic industry.

A tropical American tree introduced in India from Brazil by the Portuguese 400 years ago. It is almost naturalized in India in the coastal regions where prosperous commercial plantations exist. It is a drought resistant tree and grows well on laterite soil upto 1000m. altitude in the South.

CHAMPAK

Michelia champaca Linn. *Magnoliaceae*

Champa, Champaka (Beng./Hindi), Champakam (Mal.), Champakamu (Tel.), Shembuge (Tam.), Son champa (Mar.)

A tall stately evergreen tree usually upto 10–12m. high, sometimes reaching 30m. as in the Himalayan foot-hills. Trunk straight with greenish-brown bark, branches ascending to form a dense crown.

LEAVES : Smooth, leathery, ovate, lance-shaped. Slightly hairy on the lower side, 15–25 × 5–8cm. on a stalk which is grooved. Young buds protected by greenish bud-scale stipules.

FLOWERS : Golden-yellow 5–6cm. in size with sweet intoxicating fragrance arising singly from axils of leaves. April–Sept.

FRUIT : A cluster of woody, ovoid fruits containing angular seeds with brown or pink covering.

Usually planted for fragrant flowers and as an ornamental tree in gardens. Common all over India.

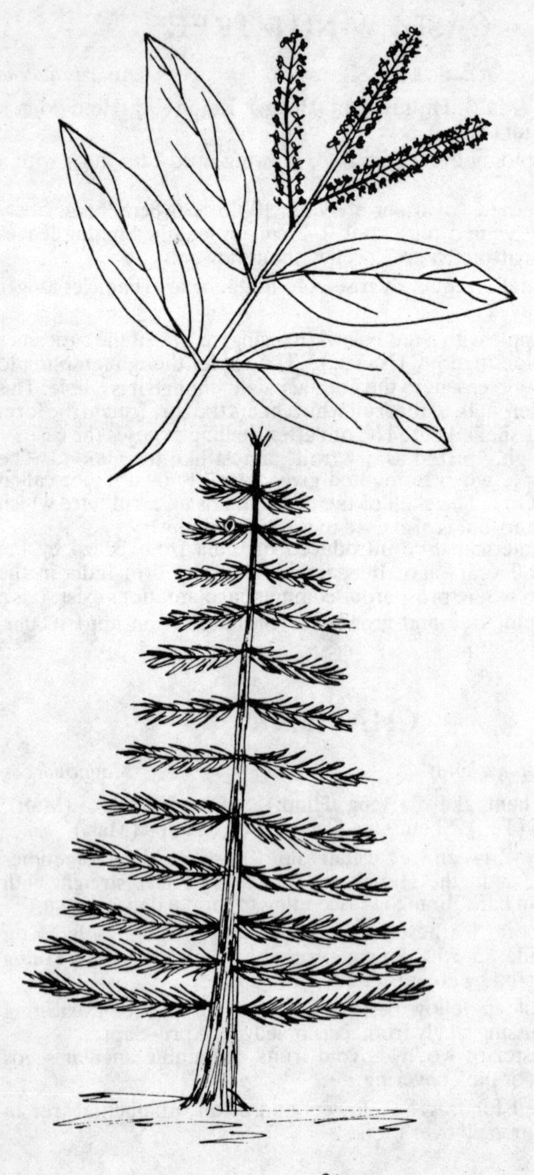

CHEBULIC MYROBALAN

Terminalia chebula Retz. *Combretaceae*

Harda (Guj.), Harra (Hindi), Haritaki (Beng.), Hirda (Mar.), Kadukkai (Tam.), Karakkai (Tel.)

A tall, profusely branched semi-deciduous tree. Bark thick, dark-brown, marked with numerous vertical cracks. Reaches upto 15m. Branches have a tendency to droop.

LEAVES : Alternate or sub-opposite, elliptic to ovate, usually pointed at the tip, rounded at base, 7–20 × 6–10cm. Stalk 2–3cm. Shedding in Feb.–March, turning red.

FLOWERS : All bisexual, white to yellowish in terminal clusters, arranged in groups of 4–6 spikes. April–Aug.

FRUIT : Ellipsoid to obovate, pendulous, variable in size, 2–6cm. long, 5-ribbed (not distinct).

Common in forests all over the plains of India and upto 1500m. Fruits contain commercial tannins and are also considered useful in indigenous medicine.

CHRISTMAS TREE

Araucaria spp. *Pinaceae*

A group of conical and showy evergreen trees with symmetrically horizontal branches reaching upto 60m., and looking strikingly elegant.

LEAVES : 1–2cm. long, needle-like, often curving inwards.

FLOWERS : There are no flowers or fruit in the normal sense but male and female cones arise on the branches. In the tropics blossoming is rather rare except in the northern latitudes.

A – cunninhami Ait is called Hoop-pine.

A – excelsa R. Br. is the Norfolk Island pine.

A – imbricata Pav is called monkey puzzle.

All of them were introduced from Australia or South Africa and are usually cultivated in parks and gardens for their evergreen elegance.

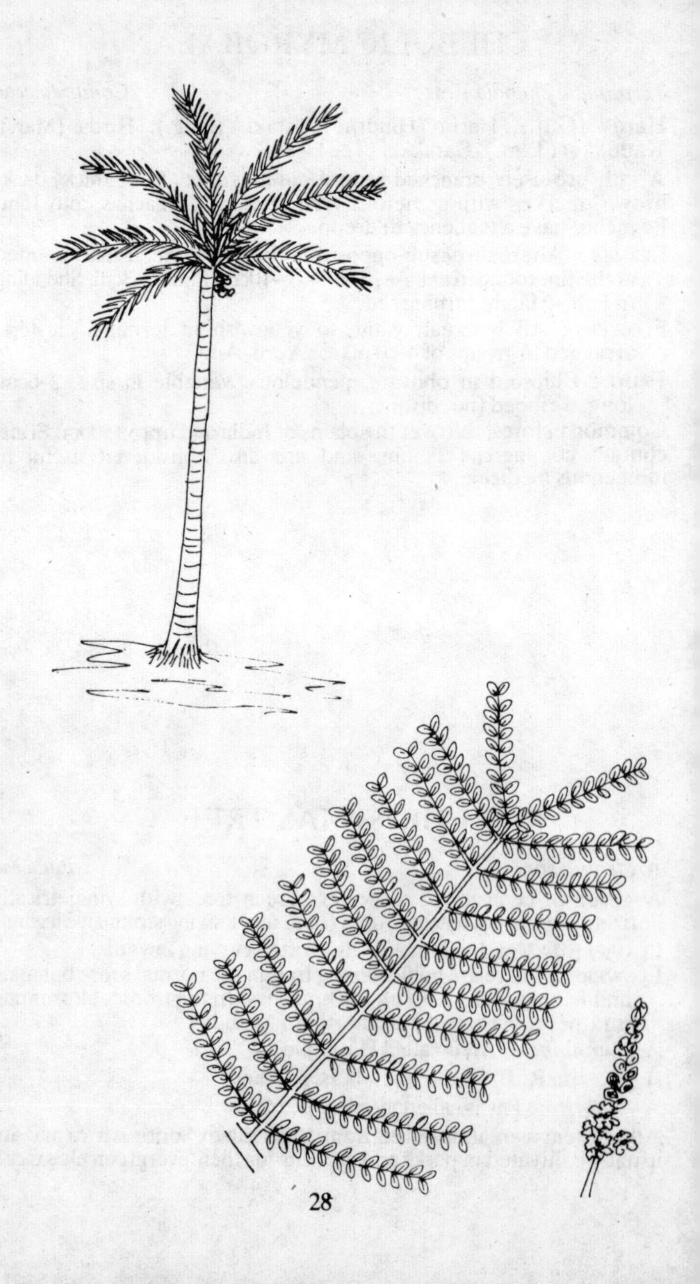

COCONUT PALM

Cocos nucifera Linn. *Arecaceae (Palmae)*

Dab (Beng.), Naral (Mar.), Nariyal (Hindi/Guj.), Narikel (Beng.), Narikelamu (Tel.), Tennaimaram (Tam.), Thenna (Mal.)

A tall, stately palm upto 25m. high, trunk with circular markings, straight or gently curved, surrounded at the base by a mass of roots.

LEAVES : Pinnate 2–6m. long with strap-shaped leaflets 60–90cm. long, narrow and tapering, swaying with breeze creating a pleasant sound.

FLOWERS : Creamy in colour, male and female on the same tree in large clusters covered by special bracts (boat shaped). Almost throughout the year.

FRUIT : Fibreous, obovoid, filled with liquid coconut milk and white copra.

Cultivated in coastal areas, all over tropical regions. The whole tree yields useful products for which it is highly valued and considered 'Kalpataru' – Wish-tree.

COPPER POD

Peltophorum pterocarpum Becker (= *P. ferrugeneum* Benth.) *Caesalpinaceae*

Ivalvagar (Tam.), Kondachinta (Tel.)

A large, semi-evergreen tree upto 30m. high, with grey, smooth bark and spreading crown and fine graceful feathery foliage.

LEAVES : Twice divided (bipinnate), dark green, 15–30cm. long with 15–20 pairs of leaflets, each with 20–30 pinnae which are deciduous, but at no time is the tree completely bare of leaves.

FLOWERS : In large erect pyramid-shaped clusters of a pale yellow colour, fragrant, covering the ground in flowering season—March to May and also often in October. Rather irregular.

FRUIT : Reddish-brown or copper-coloured pods. 5–10cm., succeed the flowers and remain on the tree for a very long time.

It is one of the commonest ornamental trees of the tropics, native in Sri Lanka, the Andamans, Malaysia. It is a fairly fast-growing tree.

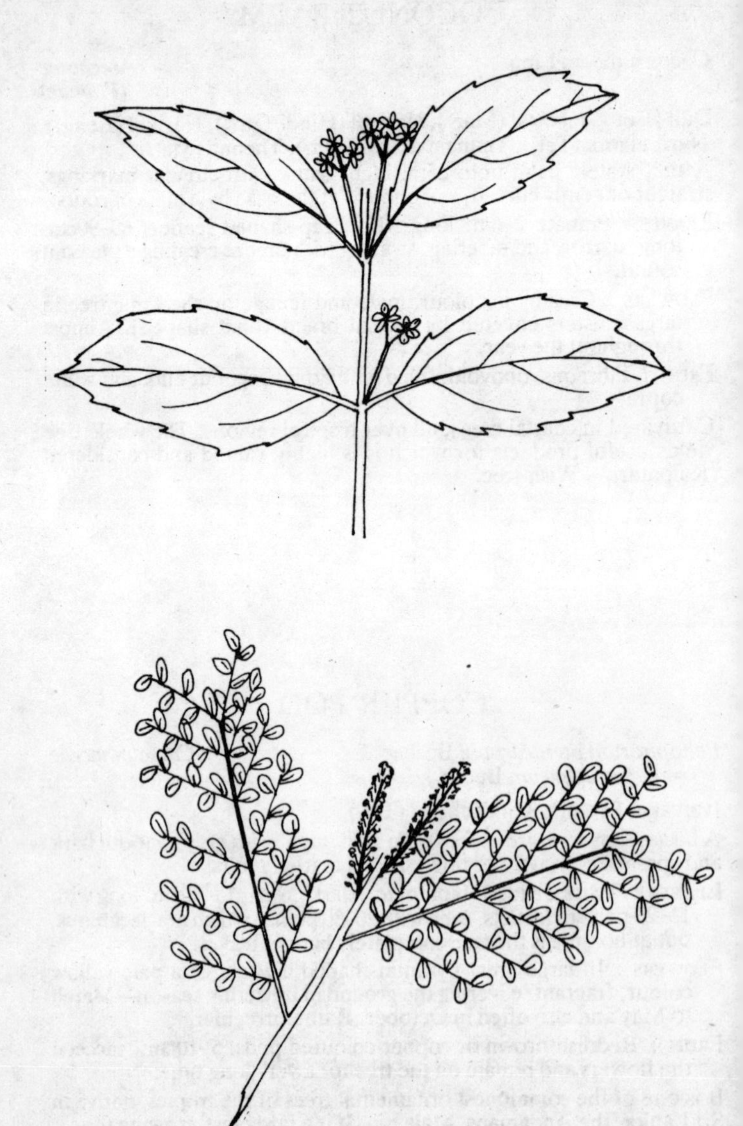

CORAL JASMINE

Nyctanthes arbortristis Linn. *Oleaceae*

Harsingar (Hindi), Parijat (Mar./Guj.), Parijatakam (Mal.), Parijatamu (Tel.), Shephalika (Beng.)

A small tree upto 10m. high. Trunk grey or greenish-white with rough bark. Branches quadrangular, covered with stiff white hair.

LEAVES : Opposite, ovate, entire or with a few large and distant teeth, 9–14 × 7cm., upper surface rough with bulbous hair, lower surface with adpressed hair.

FLOWERS : In terminal pyramidal bunches, fragrant, white with coral-orange tube. Aug.–Dec. Flowers bloom during the night and fall off in the morning.

FRUIT : A capsule, flat, obcordate, 1–6cm. across with 2 seeds.

Indigenous in north, north-east and central India. Widely cultivated for its fragrant flowers. The orange-coloured tube of the corolla was formerly used for dyeing silk.

CORALWOOD

Adenanthera pavonina Linn. *Caesalpinaceae*

Anil kundumani (Tam.), Bandiguruvenda (Tel.), Manjadi (Mal.), Moti chanothi (Guj.), Rakta kambal (Beng.), Ratan gunj, Thorli gunj (Mar.)

Moderately tall, reaching 15m.; branches ascending, bark rough, grey. Heartwood hard, coral-red.

LEAVES : Bipinnate, 20–30cm. long with 3–6 pairs of pinnae. Leaflets oblong 2–3 × 1cm., arranged evenly alternate.

FLOWERS : Yellowish, fragrant in panicle upto 25cm. long, in axis of leaves. March–May.

FRUIT : Pods 10–20cm. long, curved, containing bright, scarlet, lenticular seeds. Pods on bursting assume contortions and expose the brilliant red seeds on a silvery surface. Dispersal of seeds is carried out by birds.

Native of China, Malaya. Occurs in most parts of India though nowhere common in wild state; cultivated in parks, gardens and on roadsides.

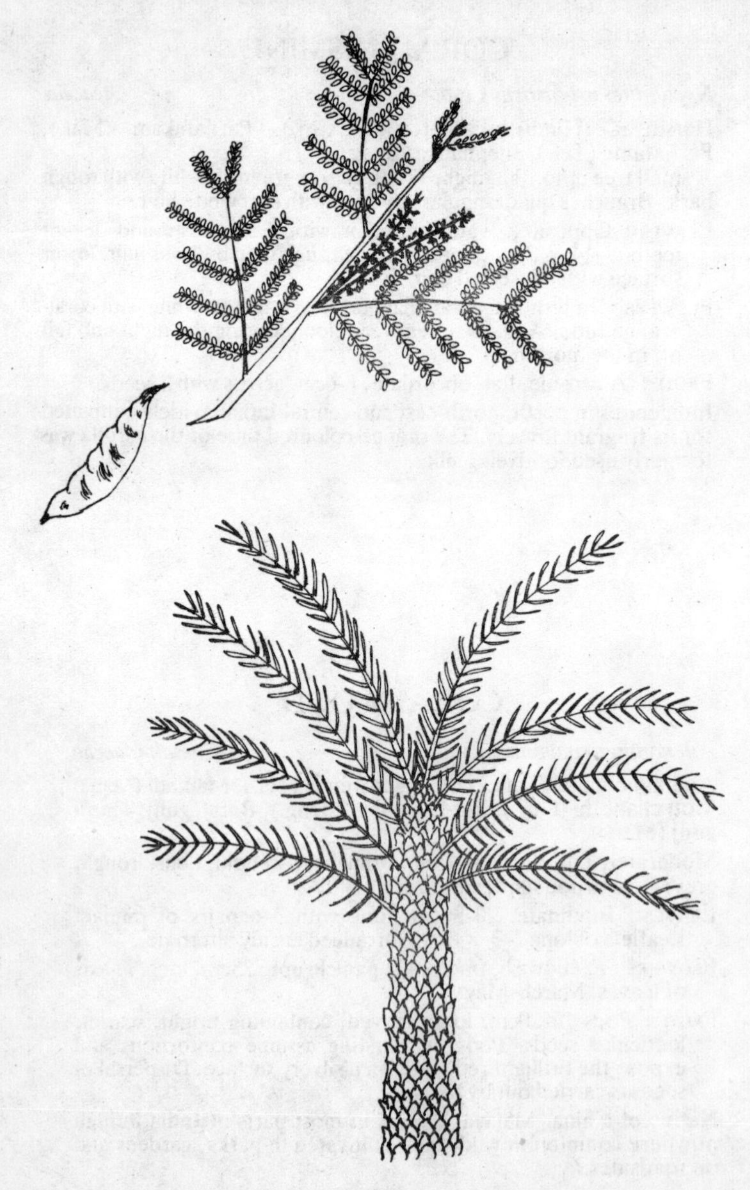

CUTCH/KHAIR

Acacia catechu Willd. *Mimosaceae*

Karangali (Tam.), Khair (Ben./Guj./Hind./Mar.), Sundra (Tel.)

Middle-sized tree (10–15m.), with dark-brown trunk and longitudinally cracked/stripping bark.

LEAVES : Twice divided (bipinnate), 15–20 pairs of leaflets and 25–50 pairs of pinnules, cup-shaped glands generally between each pair of pinnule and leaflets. Quite often the leaflets develop brownish galls in which insect eggs are laid. Pairs of spiners slightly curved and shorter (¼–½cm.)

FLOWERS : Pale yellow, minute on stalked spikes (5–10cm.), Aug.–Sept.

FRUIT : Stalked, shining, flat pod, brownish with a triangular beak at the tip.

Drier plains of India. *Acacia chundra* (Roxb.) Willd., a closely allied tree is more common in drier parts of North India. Wood yields commercial catechu used for dyeing and tanning.

CYCAS TREE

Cycas circinalis L.
& *Cycas revolutata* Thunb. *Cycadaccae*

Canningay (Tam.), Intalappana (Mal.), Jangli Madan-mast (Hindi), Kamakshi (Tel.), Madanagama (Tam.)

Hardy, very slow-growing evergreen palm-like plant of great beauty. The trunk is usually unbranched and rough. Throws out suckers and bulbils from which new plants can be propagated.

LEAVES : Large, pinnate, somewhat like those of palms, glossy green and very useful for decoration. The young leaves are pale green.

FLOWERS/FRUIT : There are no flowers in the normal sense but the male and female parts are produced on separate trees which cannot be differentiated until the reproductive organs appear. The male part is like a cone, brownish in colour, about 30–40cm. high and 15cm. in diam., made up of hundreds of units bearing pollen. The female structures take the form of a crown of fleshy, stumpy leaves bearing ovules on the sides. The seeds when ripe are pink to red about the size of a hen's egg. The reproductive organs emit a peculiar smell associated with human sex organs during orgasm, hence the origin of some of the vernacular names.

Cycas cirsinalis is common in Kerala, Orissa and Tamil Nadu. It is a popular tree cultivated in parks and gardens. *C. revoluta* Thunb.—a much smaller tree—is an introduction from China and has smaller but stiffer leaves prized for interior decoration and flower arrangement.

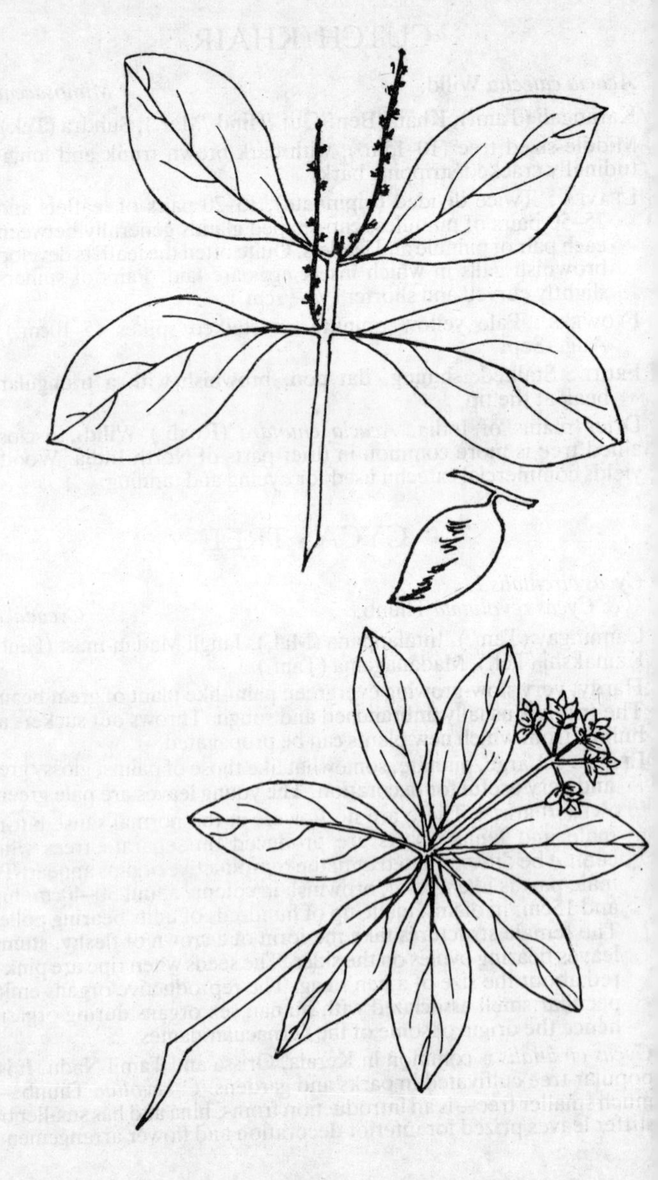

DESHI BADAM/INDIAN ALMOND

Terminalia catappa Linn. *Combretaceae*

Adamarram (Mal.), Badamachettu (Tel.), Bangla badam (Beng.), Deshi badam (Hindi), Natvadom (Tam.)

A tall, deciduous tree, branches whorled and spreading horizontally from a straight trunk. Reaches upto 15m. in height.

LEAVES : Large, shining, blunt, arising at the ends of branches. Obovate with a short stalk, 20–25 × 10–15cm. They turn a dull-red colour in the cold season before falling off.

FLOWERS : Small, white in slender spikes in the axils of leaves, about half as long as the leaves. Flowers near the top of spikes are generally male only. March–April and June–July.

FRUIT : More or less egg-sized, slightly flattened so that it is surrounded by ridges on the sides. Green turning red when ripe. Pulp edible though fibrous.

Native of Malaya, cultivated in most parts of India especially the coastal regions.

THE DEVIL TREE

Alstonia scholaris R.Br. *Apocynaceae*

Chatian (Hindi), Chattim (Beng.), Pala (Tam./Mal.), Saptaparni (Sans.)

A large, handsome evergreen tree, with buttressed trunk upto 15m. high. The bark is greyish, rough outside and yellow inside exuding latex if injured. Branches horizontal, outgoing and whorled.

LEAVES : Usually 5 to 7 in a whorl (hence the Sanskrit name Saptaparna), 10–20 × 5–6cm. oblong-lanceolate or obovate, dark green, shining above and pale with whitish bloom below, tapering on a stalk about 1cm. long.

FLOWERS : Greenish-white on long stalks radiating from a common centre in umbellate clusters. Flowers slightly villous (soft-hair). Dec.–March—occasionally throughout the year.

FRUIT : Hanging in bunches of slender pod-like sticks 30–60cm. long, giving out flattened brownish seeds with a silky fringe.

Common throughout the moister regions especially in the Western Region. The bark called 'Dita bark' is employed in native medicine. Local superstition about its devilish character arises from its poisonous properties. Almost all parts contain bitter alkaloids, and is shunned by cattle.

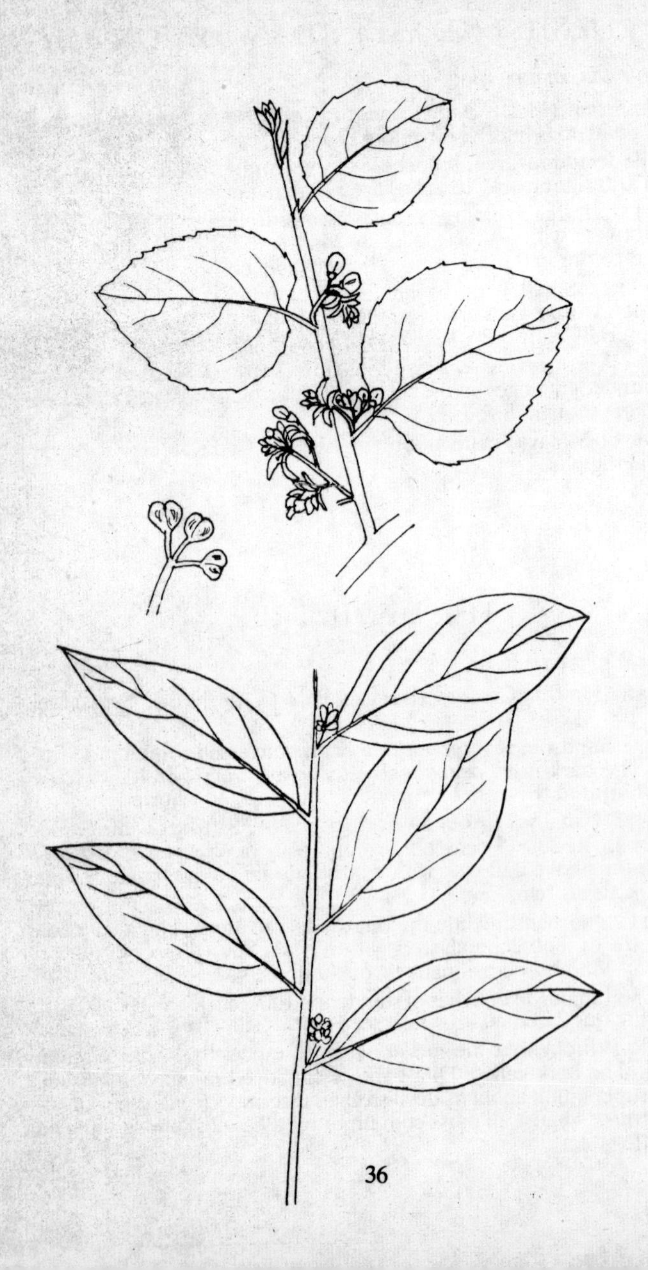

36

DHAMAN

Grewia tiliaefolia Vahl. *Tiliaceae*

Chadicha (Mal.), Charachi (Tel.), Daman, Dhaman (Hindi/Mar./Guj.), Sadachi (Tam.)

A small tree with young parts covered by star-shaped hairy scales.

LEAVES : 7–20 × 6–12cm., ovate or sub-orbicular with pointed tip, two halves of the blade unequal, margin toothed, almost smooth above, hairy below, base rounded or heart-shaped, 5–7 nerved.

FLOWERS : Yellowish in large clusters of 10–12, April–July.

FRUIT : Drupe 3–4 lobed, blackish, smooth, pea-sized.

Common in W. India in the Konkan and lower *ghats*.

An allied plant *G. asiatica* is a very variable tree, much cultivated in most parts of India for its sweetish fruits – Falsa.

DHAURA

Anogeissus latifolia Wall. *Combretaceae*

Chirimanu (Tel.), Dhaura (Guj./Mar./Hindi), Marukinchiram Mal.), Vellainaga (Tam.)

A medium-sized, gregarious, deciduous tree upto 10m. high. Trunk erect, smooth, whitish-grey, exfoliating in flakes.

LEAVES : Alternate, oblong, pale green with prominent midrib, 5–10 × 3–5cm.

FLOWERS : Dull yellow, in dense globose, axillary heads. Sept.–Jan.

FRUIT : Small, stiff, pointed, brownish in axillary heads.

very common tree in deciduous forests in warmer parts of the ountry. The trunk when bruised yields gum, 'Dhavda', used commercially in textile printing.

DILLENIA

Dillenia indica Linn. *Dilleniaceae*

Chalta (Beng./Hindi), Karambal, Karmal (Guj./Mar.), Peddakalinga, Uva (Tel.)

A medium-sized, handsome, evergreen tree, 10–20m. in height, with a dense, rounded crown. Erect trunk with straggling branches with drooping ends.

LEAVES : Arising at the ends of branches, the large leaves reach over 60cm. × 30cm. on a stalk 2–5cm. long. Outline lanceolate to ovate, sharply serrated, have numerous closely parallel veins arising laterally from the mid-rib. The upper surface is smooth and shining, the lower has prominent heavy veins. Petiole sheathing.

FLOWERS : 'Dillenia casting its enormous flowers as big as two fists' (Hooker)[5]. White, fragrant solitary with fleshy, roundish hemispherical sepals. The flowers open in June when the tree is at its leafiest.

FRUIT : Large 8–12cm. in diam. with small kidney-shaped seeds embedded in glutinous pulp. The seeds have a hairy margin.

Moist evergreen forests of the sub-Himalayan tract; also southwards in coastal regions.

Dillenia pentaphylla Roxb. is a larger deciduous tree with even larger leaves and smaller, yellower fragrant flowers about 3cm. in diam. with bark that is grey or pale brown. Also called Karmal or Karambal in the Western region. Sheds leaves in hot season, and blooms very soon. Occurs almost throughout the Indian plains in deciduous forests. It has about the largest leaves, almost as big as those of the teak or smaller banana leaves.

DRUMSTICK TREE

Moringa oleifera Lam. *Moringaceae*
(= *M. pterygosperma Gaertn.*)

Moringa (Mal.), Mulaga, Murega (Tel.), Murinna (Mal.), Marungai (Tam.), Sajina (Beng.), Sainjana, Shajna (Hindi), Shevga (Mar.)

A small to medium-sized tree upto 10m. high, deciduous, wood soft. Young parts tomentose. Bark smooth, grey.

LEAVES: Compound, thrice divided (tripinnate), pinnae and pinnules opposite, articulated (jointed) with a gland near the joint. Ultimate leaflets about 1 × 1cm., lateral ones elliptic, terminal obovate and larger. Nerves obscure.

FLOWERS : White, bisexual in large panicles, over 30cm. in length and diam., usually visited by insects. Jan.–April.

FRUIT : A long capsule 30–45cm. and 2cm. in diam., strongly ribbed, many seeded. Seeds triangular with 3 wings.

Found wild in the western Himalayas but cultivated throughout India for the edible fruits which are used in curries.

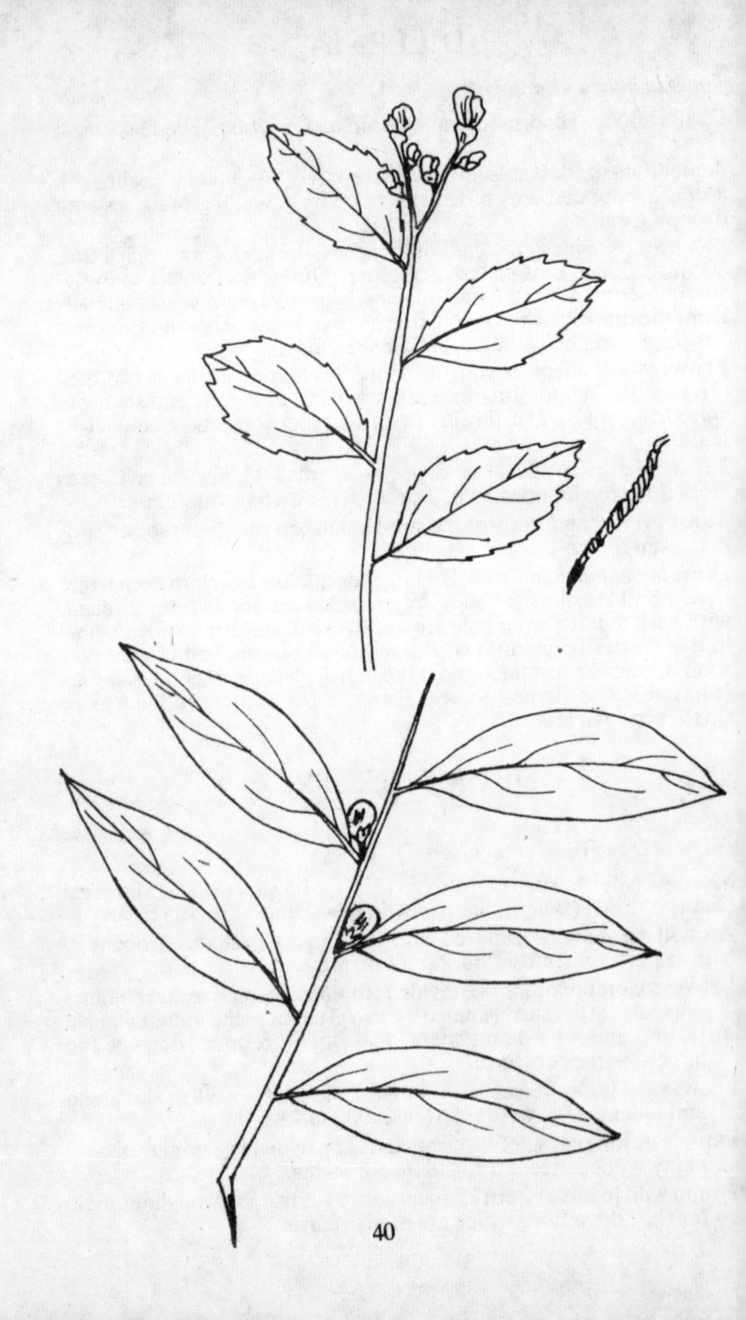

EAST-INDIAN SCREW TREE

Helicteres isora Linn. *Sterculiaceae*

Atmora (Beng.), Kaivun (Mal.), Maradphali (Hindi), Marad Sing (Guj.), Murad Sing (Mar.), Nuliti (Tel.), Valampiri (Tam.)

A shrub or small tree, 2–3m. high, rather ungainly. Branches long straggling, young shoots clothed with star-shaped hair.

LEAVES : 7–12 × 5–10cm. oblong-obovate or roundish, oblique, shortly pointed at tip, closely dotted with stellate hair on both surfaces.

FLOWERS : Very irregular, at first bright-red fading to lead colour, distinctly bilipped, 2–6 together. July–Dec.

FRUIT : Typical, consisting of 5 slender parts twisting round each other like a cristate candle.

Abundant in the deciduous forests throughout India. The fruits are considered useful in indigenous medicine.

EBONY

Diospyros melanoxylon Roxb. *Ebenaceae*

Karai (Tam.), Kari (Mal.), Temru (Guj.), Tendu (Mar./Hindi), Tumbi (Tam.), Tumki (Tel.)

A medium-sized tree upto 15m. high, trunk covered with dark brown (black) bark, peeling in large rectangular pieces, with numerous branches forming a dense crown.

LEAVES : Variable, 10–30cm. × 2–10cm., leathery, shining base tapering to a wrinkled stalk.

FLOWERS : Greenish, male in drooping clusters of 2–7 flowers; female 2–3cm. single. March–May.

FRUIT : Brown to yellowish covered with rusty hair, roundish 4–6cm., pulp sweetish, edible.

Throughout the Indian plains, in deciduous forests. Young leaves used for rolling *bidis*.

There are 2–3 allied species *D. montana* (Mountain ebony) and *D. peregrina* (Gaub) which also occur in similar habitat.

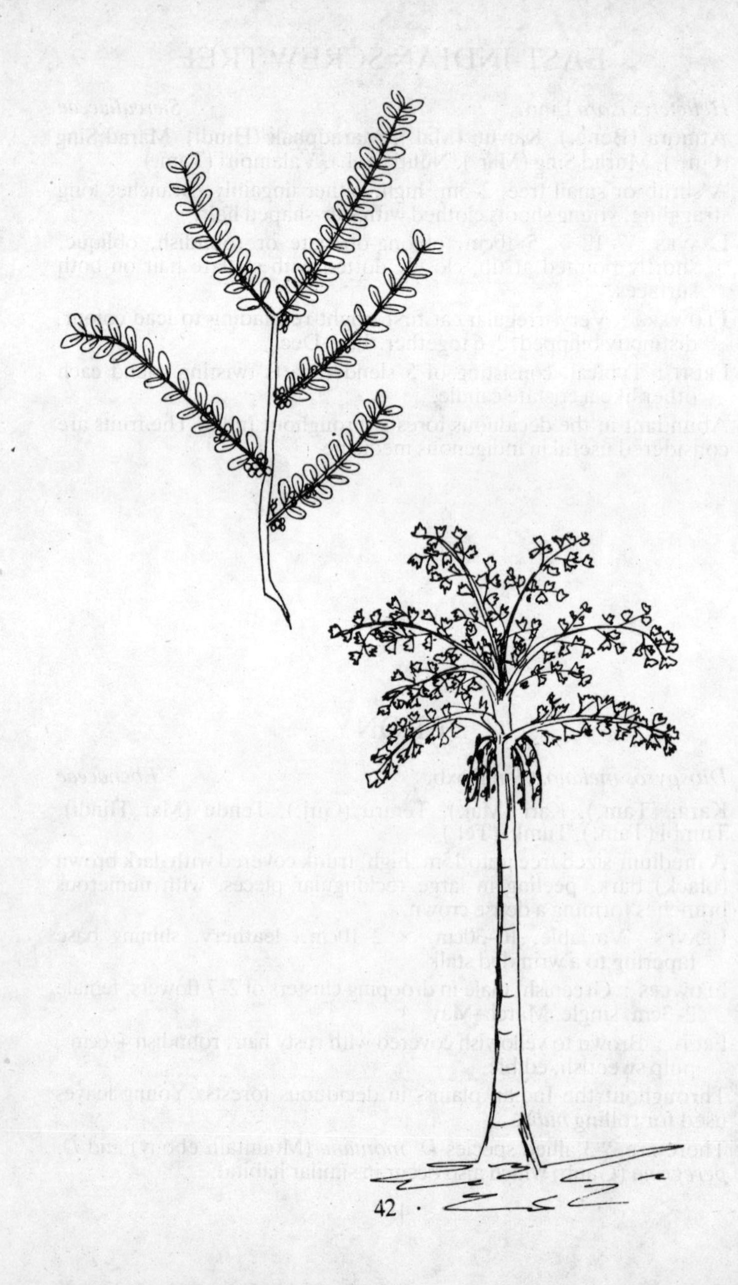

EMBLIC MYROBALAN

Emblica officinalis Gaertn. *Euphorbiaceae*

Amalaka (Kan.), Amalaki (Beng.), Amla (Guj./Hindi/Mar.), Nelli (Mal./Tam.)

A medium-sized tree (10–15m.) with a crooked trunk and spreading branches. Bark greyish-brown exfoliating in flakes.

LEAVES : Bright green, the tender ones at the tip lighter in colour, 1–1½cm., ovate, stalk very short or absent, arranged on slender branches to appear like feathery compound leaves, resembling tamarind leaves.

FLOWERS : Minute, greenish yellow, male and female separate on the same tree, arising in clusters in the axils of the tiny leaves. Feb.–May.

FRUIT : Pale yellow, globose 2–3cm. with 6 vertical furrows, fleshy, edible, sour. Very rich in Vitamin C. Highly prized in indigenous medicine.

Common in tropical, deciduous forests, often cultivated for fruit. Highly improved varieties with large tomato-sized fruit (7–9cm.) specially cultivated in northern India used in indigenous medicine.

FISH TAIL PALM

Caryota urens Linn. *Arecaceae*

Anapana (Mal.), Berli, Berlimad (Mar.), Jilugujattu (Tel.), Mari (Hindi), Shakarjata (Guj.), Tippili (Tam.)

A lofty, unbranched palm, 15–20m., may sometimes even reach 30m. Trunk smooth, cylindrical with ring-like markings, fairly smooth and grey.

LEAVES : Very large, bipinnate, reaching upto 5–6m. in length and 40cm. in breadth. The leaflets are like a fish tail or fin, serrated at the tip.

FLOWERS : The tree flowers after about 10–15 years. The flowers are borne on large bunches of heavy pendulous spikes 3–7m. long bearing both male and female flowers.

FRUIT : Roundish about 2cm. in diam., reddish with 1–2 seeds, which appear like a split or half areca nut.

Very common in evergreen forests, throughout warmer parts. The trees are tapped for toddy.

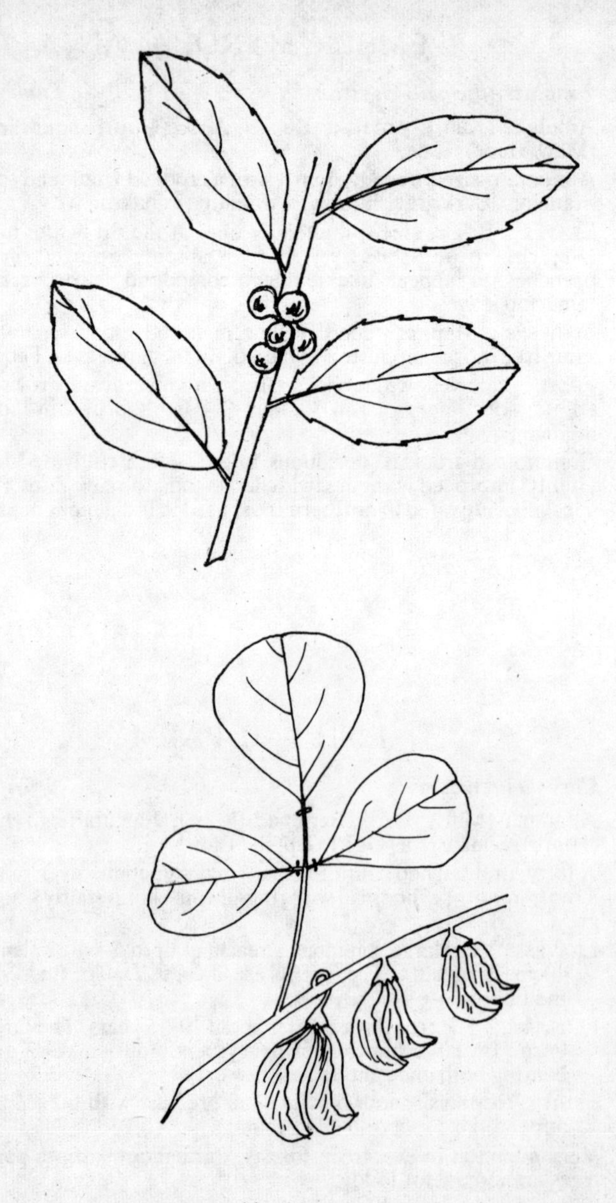

FLACOURTIA

Flacourtia montana Grah. *Flacourtiaceae*

Attak (Mar.), Benchi (Beng.), Kondai (Hind.), Lodri (Guj.), Tambat (Mar.)

A small thorny, deciduous tree upto 10m. high.

LEAVES : Alternate, elliptic 3–5 nerves, from base 12–18 × 3–8cm., shining with toothed margin.

FLOWERS : Creamy white, in velvety clusters, Nov.–Dec.

FRUIT : Reddish, cherry-like, edible, sour. Greatly relished by birds and squirrels.

Common in deciduous forests on lower hill regions. Some forms have very few thorns. Several allied species, viz. *F. ramonchii*—Madagascar plum—are cultivated and *F. sepiaria* a rigid shrub occurs wild in Kumaon, Bengal, Bihar, Orissa in deciduous forests.

FLAME OF THE FOREST

Butea monosperma (Lam.) Kuntze *Papilionaceae*
(= *B. frondosa* Koenig)

Dhak (Hindi), Khakharo (Guj.), Palas (Hindi/Beng./Mar./Mal.), Parasa (Tam.)

A medium-sized, deciduous tree upto 10–12m. high. Its irregular branching makes it an unattractive tree when not in flower. Trunk covered with ash-coloured, rough bark.

LEAVES : Trifoliate, young leaves very delicately tomentose. Old leaves hairless above and finely silky below which gives them a peculiar greyish appearance when seen from a distance. Terminal leaflet 10–15 × 7–10cm. Laterals, slightly smaller, oblique. Main stalk 10–15cm. long. Leaf fall begins from Nov. upto Dec.–Jan.

FLOWERS : Groups in threes on velvety, olive-green stalk about 15cm. long. Petals flaming orange covered by silky hair. Blackish flower-buds begin to appear in January. Bloom till April, like patches of fire in a leafless scrub forest, hence '*Flame of the forest*'.

FRUIT : Young pods, flat, pale green, turning brown on drying, covered by white to grey tomentum. One seed enclosed near the tip.

Common throughout India. Described in mythological and literary Sanskrit works. Slow-growing, gives sustenance to many types of insects, including the lac insect.

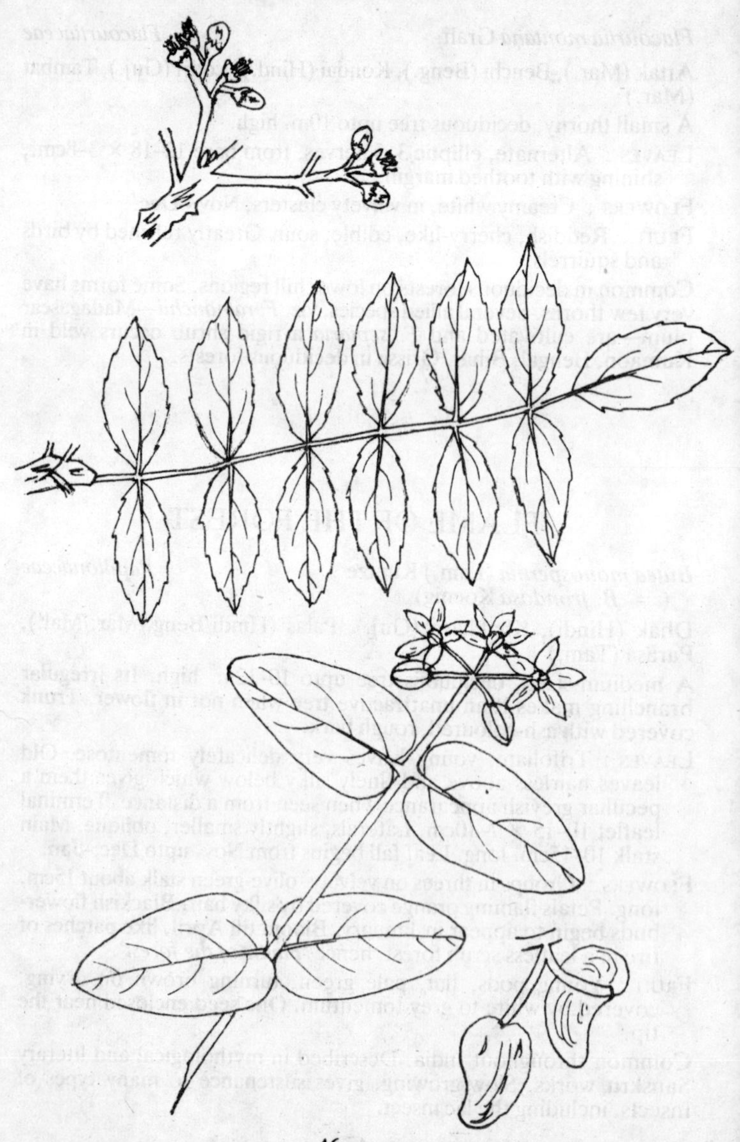

GARUGA

Garuga pinnata Roxb. *Burseraceae*

Halabalage (Kan.), Jum (Beng.), Kakad (Mar.), Karrevembu (Tam.), Kharpat (Hindi), Khusemb (Guj.), Kosramba (Mal.)

A medium-sized tree (upto 10m.), deciduous, bark brownishgreen, peeling in large irregular flakes.

LEAVES : Compound, alternate, 15–45cm. long, with 6–10 pairs of leaflets and an odd one. Leaflets, elliptic, hairy, most often covered with green, brown or red galls giving an appearance of fruit.

FLOWERS : Yellowish-white, in hairy, loosely branched, clusters arising at the top of leafless branches. Feb.–Apr.

FRUIT : Yellowish, globular, about 2cm. in diam. Sour, edible, often cooked with fish curry in coastal regions (Goa).

Found in many parts of the lower hills and plains throughout India.

GIANT MILKWEED

Calotropis gigantea R. Br. *Asclepiadaceae*

Ak (Hindi), Akanda (Beng.), Ankado (Guj.), Arkam (Tam.), Erikku (Mal.), Jilledu (Tel.), Rui (Mar.)

One of the commonest shrubs, reaches tree-size if allowed to grow. Trunk and branches yellowish-white, furrowed. Young branches covered with cottony pubescence. Profusely milky.

LEAVES : 10–12 × 4–10cm. opposite, sessile, elliptic-oblong, acute, thick, glaucous-green, underside with cottony pubescence profusely milky.

FLOWERS : Inodorous, purplish-white, 3–5cm. in diam., in flat-topped clusters, arising from a stout stalk. Each flower has a central crown. A white-flowered variant is rather rare.

FRUIT : In paired boat-shaped capsules, about 8–10cm., bursting when dry and exposing a large number of brown, flattened seeds with silky kapok attached at one end. The arrangement of the seeds in a young fruit — arranged like fish-scales — is fascinating to observe.

Common all over the plains particularly on wasteland. Almost always in flower. Considered sacred by Hindus. *C. procera*, an allied species with slightly smaller flowers and flattish crown occurs in drier regions and deserts.

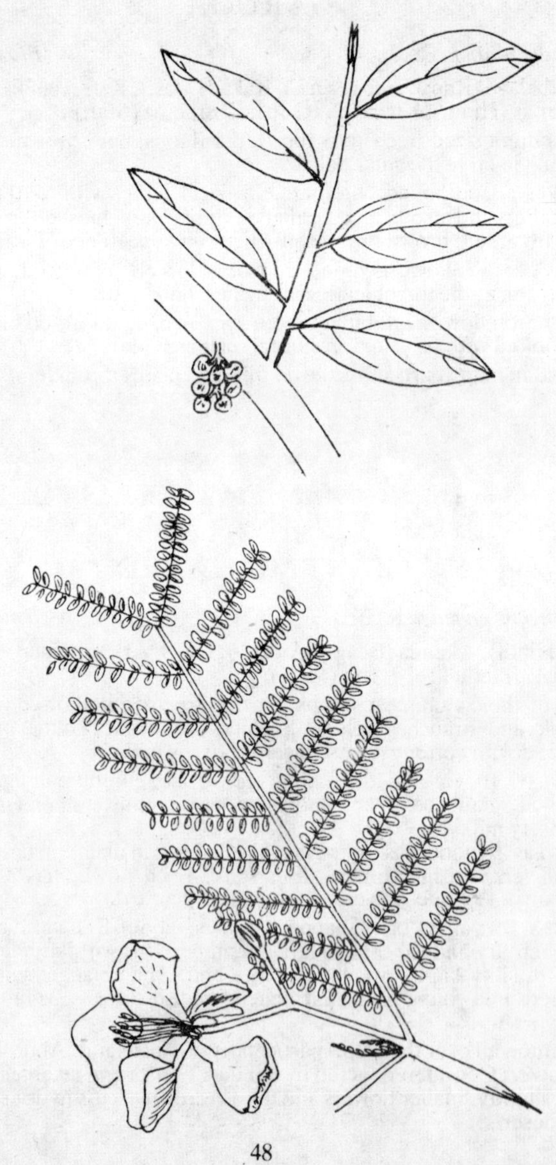

GULAR

icus glomerata Roxb. *Moraceae*
(= *F. racemosa* Linn.)

Athi (Kan./Mal.), Atti (Tel.), Damur (Beng.), Gular (Hindi/Guj.), Jdumbaramu (Tel.), Umbar (Mar./Guj.)

A common tree growing up to 50m. with age. The trunk is straight nd smooth in younger trees which may be gnarled but smooth when ld.

LEAVES : 8–20 × 3–7cm. ovate, oblong or lance-shaped when ripe covered by galls.

FLOWERS : Inconspicuous, inside the unripe figs.

FRUIT : Clusters of figs on the trunk and main branches, reddish when ripe, infested with insects.

This tree is common both in the hills and plains. It is frequently found ear water-courses. The bark is considered useful in indigenous nedicine.

GULMOHUR

elonix regia Rafin. *Caesalpinaceae*
= *Poinciana regia* Bojer)

lamboyant (Eng.), Gul Mohur (Hindi/Mar./Beng./Guj.), Mayurum Tam.), Bhima Sankesula (Tel.)

One of the most popular, quick-growing, deciduous tree, reaching pto 15m. Bark slightly rough, greyish brown, branches spreading.

EAVES : Feathery, bipinnate, upto 60cm. long, composed of 11–18 pinnae. Each pinna bears 20–30 pairs of small oblong leaflets, dancing with breeze. Leaf-fall between Feb.–March. New leaves appear in early June.

LOWERS : Appear with the onset of hot weather and the whole tree is a blaze of scarlet bloom in April-May. Flowers in immense clusters at the ends of branches. One of the petals is slightly larger and variegated in colour. Chiefly pollinated by birds.

RUIT : Pods flat, green when young, harden with age, turn deep brown and remain for a long time on the tree. 30–60cm. long. Seeds oblong and transversely mottled.

ative of Madagascar, introduced to India and grown throughout the opics. 'The very embodiment of the spirit of the east, beautiful but ild looking and seductive.' (Ida Colthurst).[6]

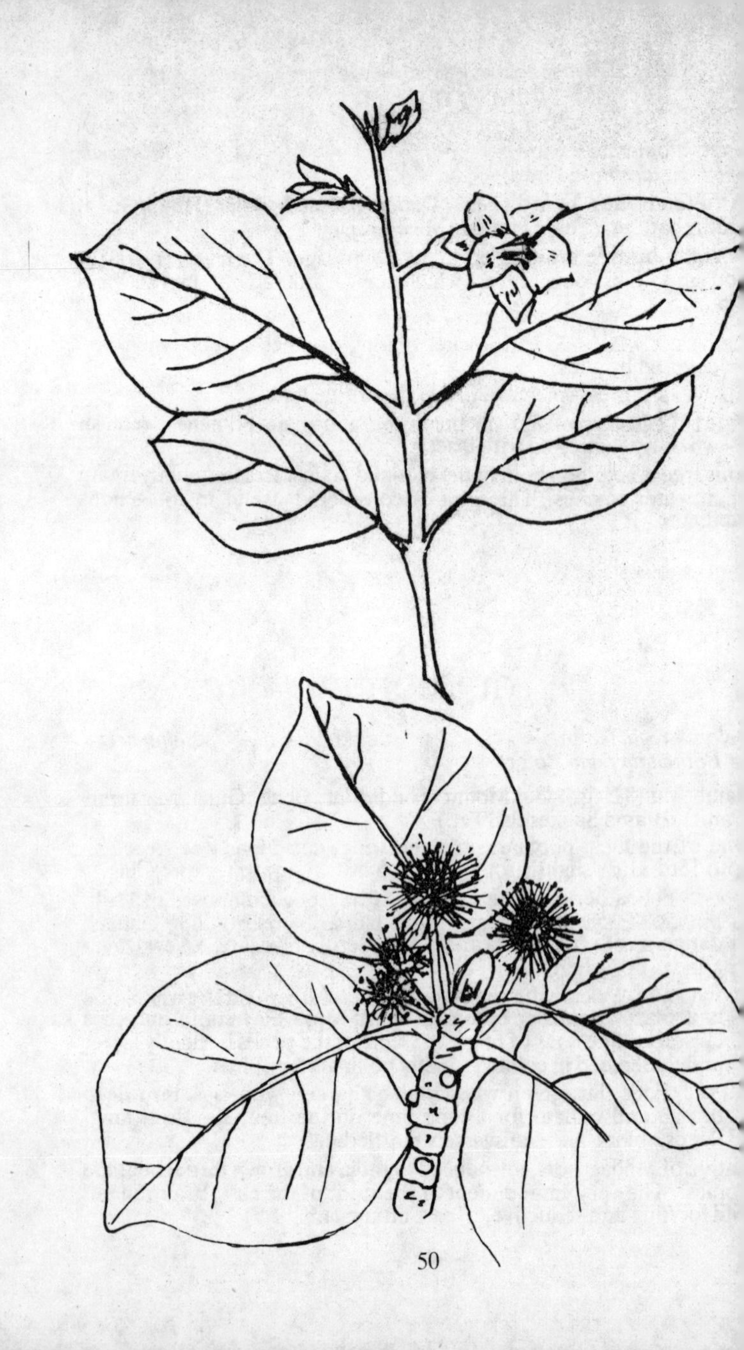

'GUMHAR'/WHITE TEAK

Gmelina arborea Roxb. *Verbenaceae*

Gambhar, Gumbar (Beng.), Gumhar (Hindi), Gummadi (Tel.), Kumadi (Tam.), Kumbil (Mal.), Shewan (Mar./Guj.)

A deciduous tree 10–20m. high. Trunk straight, branches horizontal, bark greyish-yellow, rather corky; young parts clothed with silky hair.

LEAVES : Opposite, ovate with elongated tip, entire, glabrous, often with glandular spots at the base of the leaf-blade, undersurface pubescent, 10–20 × 10–13cm.

FLOWERS : Greenish-yellow arising in terminal panicles about 25cm. in size. Feb.–May.

FRUIT : A fleshy, orange-yellow date-like fruit enclosing 1–2 oblong seeds.

It occurs in coastal regions and the Himalayan tract; also in dry deciduous regions of central India. Its timber is excellent. It is one of the very fast-growing trees.

HALDU

Adina cordifolia Hook. *Rubiaceae*

Haldu (Hindi/Guj.), Heddi (Mar.), Manja-Kadamba (Tam./Mal.), Pasupa-Kadamba (Tel.), Petpuria (Beng.)

A stout tree upto 10–20m. high. Trunk erect, branches horizontal, bark brownish-grey, furrowed.

LEAVES : 20–25cm. long, almost as broad, heart shaped at base with a pointed tip. Crown shaped stipules covering a young bud at the tip of the branch.

FLOWERS : In buff-coloured spheres, 2–4cm., containing numerous small flowers. Mar.–May.

FRUIT : Round, black ball-like structure.

Dry forests throughout the hilly parts of India.

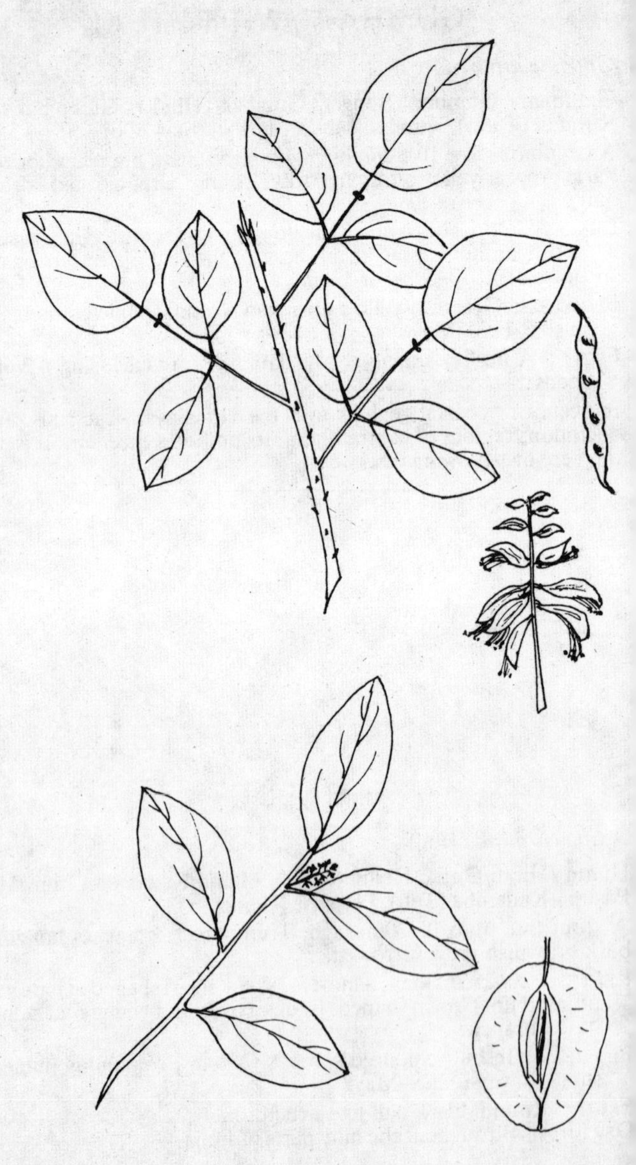

INDIAN CORAL

Erythrina indica Lam. *Papilionaceae*

Badisa, Badita (Tel.), Kalyana Mukikku (Mal.), Mandara (Hindi), Palita Mandar (Beng.), Panervo (Guj.), Pangara (Mar.)

A middle-sized, deciduous tree upto 20m. Trunk and branches smooth but studded with small, dark prickles.

LEAVES : 3-foliate, 15–50cm.; leaflets triangular. Odd leaftlet larger than the other two. All leaves begin to fall in the cold season.

FLOWERS : Crimson, on a long stalk, arranged in conical formation at the tip of branches. Each pea-flower (Papilionaceous) 5–7cm. long. Rich with nectar, the flowers are visited by a large number of noisy birds and insects. Feb.–May.

FRUIT : A long, beaded pod, 15–20cm. with 5–7 seeds.

Common in beach forests and deciduous forests. A white-flowered variety is often cultivated in gardens. A closely allied species *E. stricta* Roxb, very similar in appearance, has shorter, non-beaded pods.

INDIAN ELM/KANJU (Trade)

Holoptelia integrifolia Planch. *Ulmaceae*

Aval (Mal.), Aya (Tam.), Kanju (Hindi), Kanjho (Guj.), Thapasi (Tel.), Vavla (Mar.)

A tall deciduous tree 15–20m. high, sometimes with buttressed base. Bark grey with pustules, branches spreading.

LEAVES : 8–12 × 3–6cm., elliptic, point elongated, margin entire, smooth, base rounded.

FLOWERS : Male and female mixed in pyramidal clusters. Feb.–March.

FRUIT : Almost rounded 2–3cm., flat like a coin, winged with centre containing a seed. The fruits rain down in the breeze during May–June.

Common tree in deciduous forests all over India.

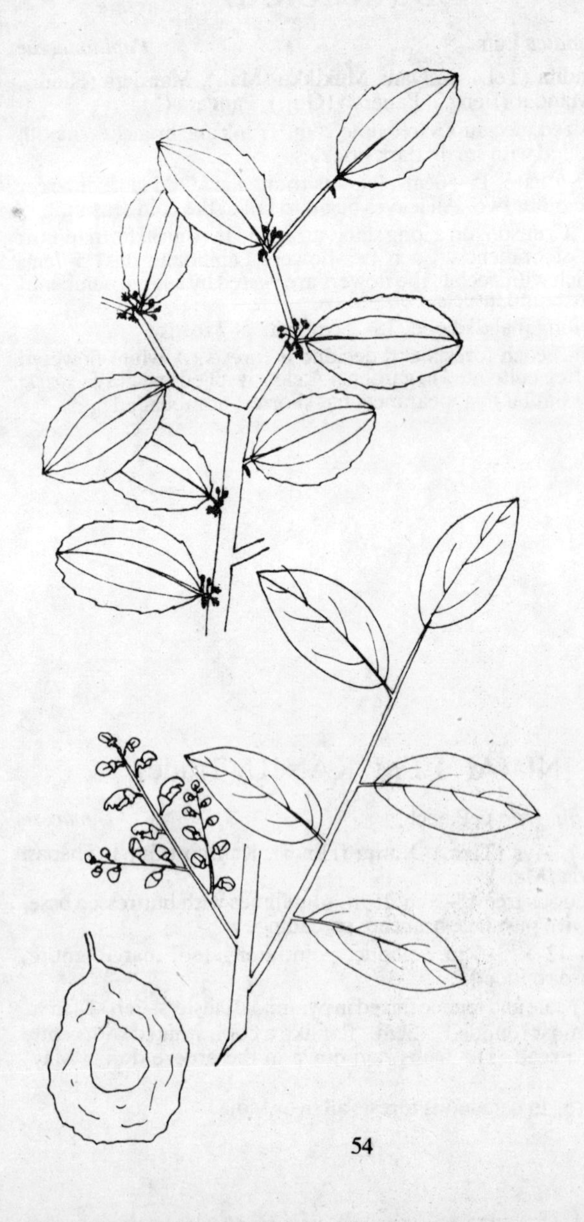

INDIAN JUJUBE

Zizyphus mauritiana Lam. *Rhamnaceae*
(= *Z. jujube* Lam., non Mill.)

Ber (Hindi), Bor (Guj., Mar.), Boroi (Beng.), Elandai (Tam.), Elentha (Mal.), Reegu (Tel.)

A small evergreen tree, variable in size upto 10m. in height, with grey r dull black rough, cracked bark.

LEAVES : Variable, oblong-elliptic, ovate, closely serrate or entire, rominently 3–nerved with 2 stipular spines, one of which is hooked.

FLOWERS : Small, greenish-yellow in axils.

FRUIT : Drupe, oblong, globose, ovoid, red or orange or yellowish with one hard seed.

Found both wild and cultivated throughout the greater part of India. The larger fruits are generally produced on grafted plants in which *Z. umularia* or *Z. jujuba* Mill. is used as stock and better varieties are rafted on them.

INDIAN KINO / MALABAR KINO

Pterocarpus marsupium Roxb. *Papilionaceae*

Bibla (Mar.), Bija, Bijasal (Hindi), Biyo, Hira dakhan (Guj.), Venga Mal.), Vengai (Tam.), Yegi (Tel.)

A large deciduous tree upto 15–20m. high. The straight bole with preading branches covered by thick yellowish-grey, corky bark with ongitudinal fissures. Exfoliates in heavy scales exposing rusty inner bark from which a blood-red gum (Gum Kino) exudes.

LEAVES : Alternate, imparipinnate, leaflets 5–7, elliptic-oblong, 8 × 5cm., shiny.

FLOWERS : Yellowish, scented, in large panicles 8–11cm. long appearing in May-June. Visited by swarms of bees. 'All day the air is a savoury intoxication while in their vicinity. At dusk the flowers fall forming by morning a thick, yellow carpet under the trees.' (Ida Colthurst).[7]

FRUIT : Orbicular, flat like a big coin, with a circular wing, upto 5cm. in diam. with 1–2 convex bony seeds.

Indigenous to India, common in deciduous forests all over India. The gum (Kino) is used in dyeing, tanning and printing.

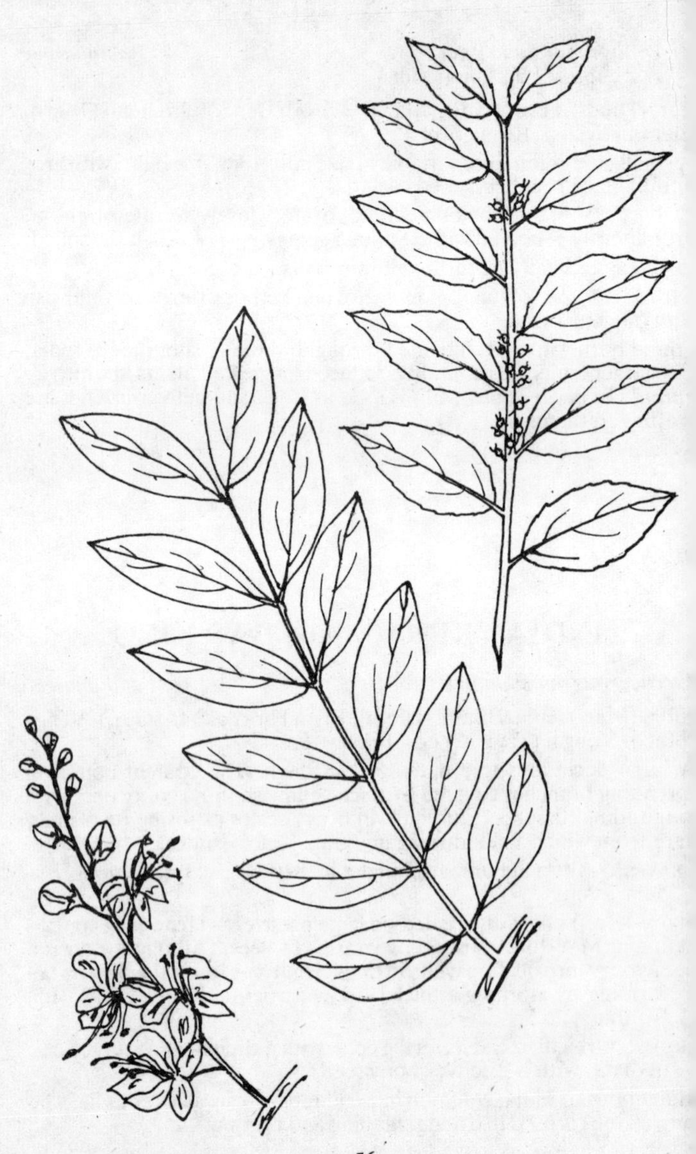

INDIAN LABURNUM

Cassia fistula Linn. *Caesalpinaceae*

Amaltas (Hindi/Beng.), Bhava (Mar.), Garmalo (Guj.), Konnei (Tam.), Rela (Tel.), Sondal, Sundali (Beng.)

A medium-sized, deciduous tree reacing upto 10m. Bark smooth and ash coloured in young trees, rough and dark brown in old trees. Branches slender, drooping.

LEAVES : Compound, pinnate, 20–40cm. long, bearing 4–8 pairs of leaflets. Each leaflet 5–12 × 4–9cm., smooth, bright green above and covered with silvery hair below. New leaves appear between April–May, the tree being leafless in Feb.–March.

FLOWERS : Arranged in drooping racemes 30–45cm. long, bearing bright yellow, fragrant bunches of flowers with some resemblance to the English laburnum. April–June.

FRUIT : Straight, cylindrical pods, 30–100cm., about 2–3cm. in diam. Smooth, green, turning dark brown or black with age. Contain 40–100 oval, shining, yellowish-brown seeds, embedded in dark, sweetish pulp.

Common in deciduous forests all over India upto 1500m. Various parts of the tree are used in indigenous medicine. Golden-yellow patches of flowers when the forest is almost leafless.

INDIAN NETTLE TREE

Trema orientalis Blume *Urticaceae*

Ama (Mal.), Ambaratthi (Tam.), Budamuru (Tel.), Chikan (Beng.), Gio (Hindi), Gol (Mar./Guj.), Jilan (Beng.)

A small tree, almost evergreen, reaching upto 10m. Trunk straight, branches horizontal, tender ones pubescent.

LEAVES : 6–12 × 3–4cm. obliquely ovate, with an elongated point, margin roundly toothed to serrate, rough above, softly pubescent below, base subcordate (heart shaped).

FLOWERS : Male and female on the same or different trees in hairy clusters, male in greenish compact masses and females in loose clusters. Almost all the year round.

FRUIT : Rounded, about ½cm. in diam., black when ripe.

It is fast-growing tree, preferring disturbed, that is, well aerated soil. Rather short-lived.

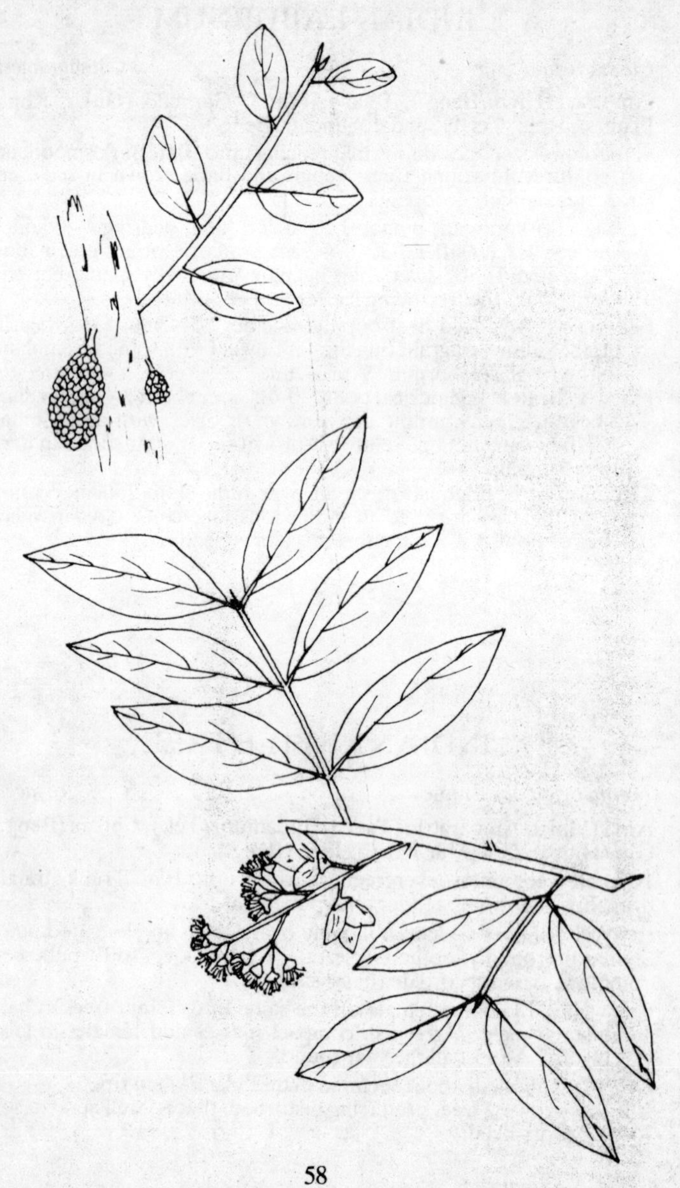

JACK FRUIT

Artocarpus integra (Thumb.) Merrill *Urticaceae*
(= *Artocarpus heterophylla* Linn.)

Chakka (Mal.), Kanthal (Beng.), Kathal (Hindi), Panas (Tel.), Phanas (Mar.), Pilapalam (Tam.)

An evergreen tree (10–15m.) with a dark trunk and dense crown of shiny foliage. Older trees often gnarled with huge fruits hanging from the trunk.

LEAVES : Milky, alternate, elliptic, shiny above with large stipule (covering the bud) that soon falls off.

FLOWERS : Unisexual, minute, male in slender drooping, limpish, long, finger-like projections coming out from branches. Female flowers in roundish ball like clusters from the trunk and larger branches. Nov.–Jan.

FRUIT : Huge 30–50 × 20–30cm., oblong, hanging on short stalks is a sight which inspires awe.

Common in moister parts of India. Normally cultivated, seldom seen wild. Several varieties are recognized in the Goa region.

JAMUN

Syzygium cuminii (Linn.) Skeels *Myrtaceae*
(= *Eugenia jambolana* Linn.)

Jam (Beng.), Jaman, Jamun (Hindi/Mar.), Jambu (Guj.), Kala jam (Hindi), Naval (Mal.) Neereedu (Tel.), Neredam (Tam.)

A large handsome tree except in the hills. Trunk covered with light-coloured peeling bark.

LEAVES : Opposite, elliptic-oblong, leathery, smooth, shining, typical Jambul scent when crushed (gland-dotted). Veins unite in a clear intra-marginal nerve running from base to the tip of the leaf.

FLOWERS : Creamish, fragrant, in heavy clusters. March–June.

FRUIT : Purplish black, ovoid, 2–5cm., edible.

Very well known and easily grown all over India. Variable in size. Crooked and stunted in the hills as in Mahabaleshwar, where it is very common at 1500m. altitude.

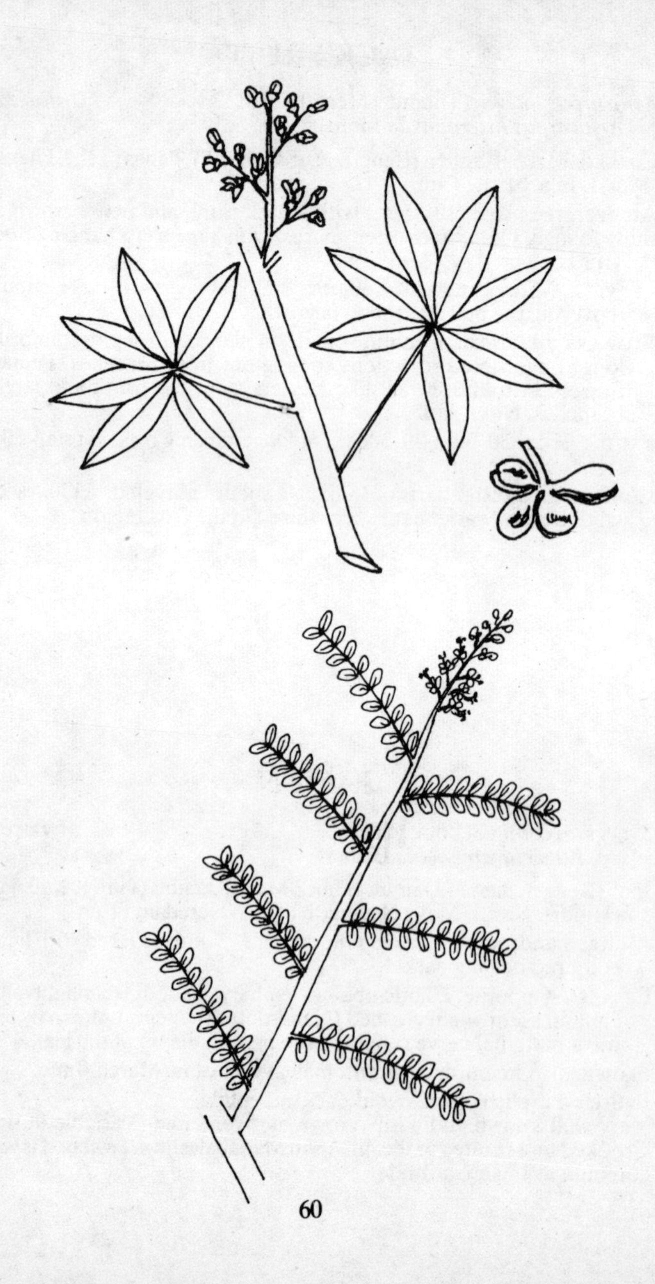

JANGLI BADAM

Sterculia foetida Linn. *Sterculiaceae*

Gurapabadamu (Tel.), Jangli badam (Hindi/Mar./Guj./Beng.), Pottakavalam (Mal./Tam.)

A tall, majestic tree usually planted on roadsides or in parks. The straight clean bole with a crown of radiating horizontal branches lends considerable grace to the tree. Bark brownish, flaking off.

LEAVES : Palmate or digitate with 5–9 leaflets. Each leaflet 10–18 × 3–5cm., oblong, lance-shaped with pointed tip. Leaf-stalk 15–24cm., grooved. Leaves crowded near the ends of branches.

FLOWERS : 2–4cm., reddish, male and female separate, foetid smell, arising in pyramidal clusters 15–20cm. long. March–May, Oct.–Dec.

FRUIT : Bright red when ripe, woody, in 4–5 units which are boat-shaped. Seeds edible as inferior substitute for almonds.

'A roof of dark green glory but emitting an intolerable smell when in bloom' (Sir Edwin Arnold).[8]
Distance makes the smell not only tolerable but even pleasant.

JAVA CASSIA

Cassia javanica Linn. *Caesalpinaceae*

A medium-sized tree, with a straight trunk upto 15m. high, bark smooth, dark brown, branches spreading, sturdy with an umbrella-like canopy.

LEAVES : Feathery, 15 × 30cm. long, composed of 8–14 pairs of leaflets. Leaflets 3–5cm. long, short-stalked, oblong-oval, rounded at the tip, smooth and silky to touch. Leaf fall commences in Dec. and the tree is bare in Feb. New leaves appear in May.

FLOWERS : Pink, in clusters of about 10 blooms on long slender stalks; appear with new leaves in May.

FRUIT : Cylindrical pods 35–60cm. long, containing 70–80 smooth, shiny, brown pea-sized, flattened seeds. Ripens Feb.

Native of Sumatra and Java, cultivated on roadsides and gardens in the Indian plains for its abundance of flowers. Comparatively short-lived.

JAVA FIG

Ficus comosa Roxb. *Moraceae*
(= *Ficus benjamina* L. var *comosa*)

A hardy medium-sized fig tree with slender hanging roots. The roots do not form columns or props as in the Banyan and so the tree does not spread as much.

LEAVES : Glossy, leathery, broadly ovate, which look graceful on drooping branches.

FLOWERS : Inconspicuous, contained inside the immature figs; mainly in March–April.

FRUIT : In the form of figs about the size of a pea, smooth, yellowish-green with purplish spots, sessile. Generally relished by birds.

It is often cultivated as an avenue tree. It is also fancied by Bonsai enthusiasts in the tropics as a suitable plant for their artistic pursuit.

JHINGAN

Llanea coromandelica (Houtt) Merrill.
(= *L. grandis* Endl. *Anacardiaceae*
= *Odina wodier* Roxb.)

Appriyada (Tel.), Jiyal (Beng.), Jhingan (Hindi), Moi (Mar.), Odiya Maram (Mal.), Wodier (Tam.)

A deciduous, medium-sized tree upto 10m. high, trunk smooth, ash-coloured, bark cracking and peeling off when old. Masses of gum exudes from wounds and cracks.

LEAVES : Compound, alternate 25–45cm. long, leaflets 3–5 pairs and an odd one longer than others, pink when young, green above and brown below when dry.

FLOWERS : Small yellowish-purplish, male and female alike but in separate clusters when the tree is leafless. Dec.–Apr.

FRUIT : Red when ripe, ½–2cm., kidney-shaped.

Widely distributed in deciduous forests.

'A handsome tree in full foliage, an eyesore when leafless' (Brandis).[9]

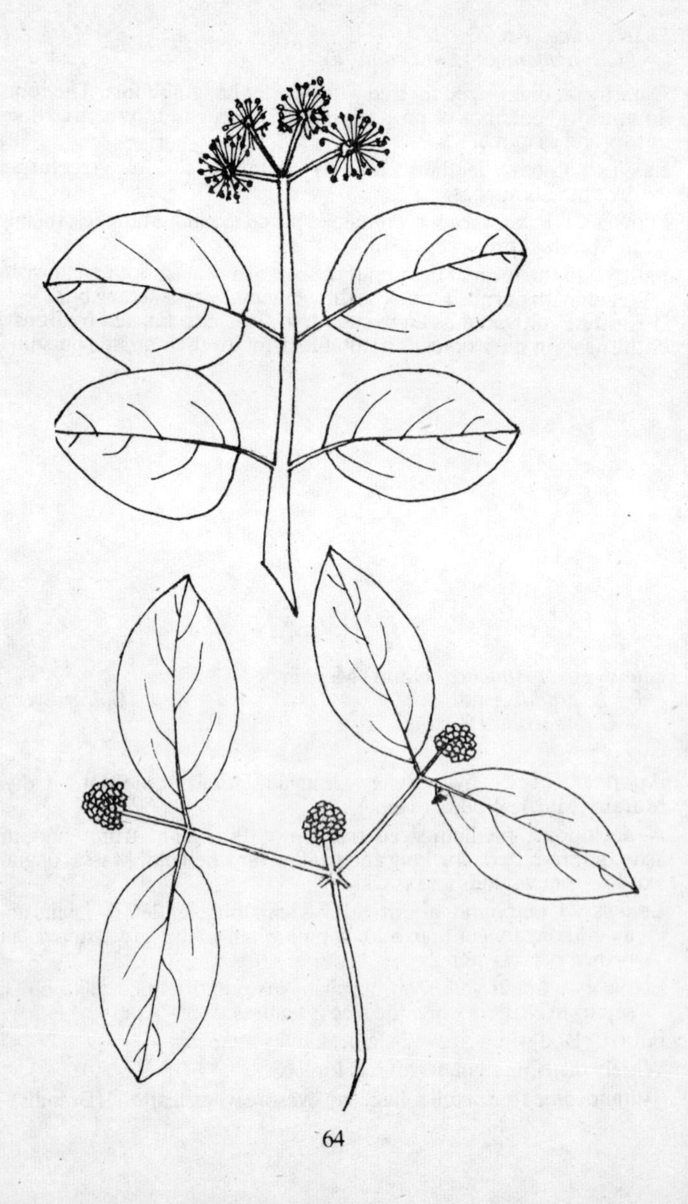

KADAM(BA) TREE

Anthocephalus cadamba Miq. *Rubiaceae*

Attutek (Mal.), Kadamba (Beng./Guj./Hindi/Mar.); Kadambamu Tel.)

A large deciduous tree with a straight bole upto 20m. high. Bark ntact, greyish.

EAVES : Long-stalked, cordate-ovate 15–20 × 8–10cm. (young leaves much bigger), stipules prominent between young leaves, falling off when leaves mature.

LOWERS : Yellowish in globose heads, about 3–4cm. in diam. June–July.

RUIT : Size of a small orange. Creamy-yellow.

t is a fast-growing tree. The flowers are harbingers of rain. Held in reat reverence by Hindus, being associated with the pranks of Lord rishna when young.

KAIM

Iytragyna parviflora Kunth. *Rubiaceae*

hinna Kadambu (Tam.), Guli Kadam (Beng.), Kaim, Kalmi (Hindi), alamb (Mar.), Nir Kadambe (Tel.), Nir Kadambu, Vimbu (Mal.)

nearly smooth tree, evergreen, with a short buttressed trunk, reyish bark peeling off in scales.

EAVES : Opposite, variable, oblong, base rounded 5–12 × 4–7cm. Stipules 1cm. at the tip of the branch, falling off early.

LOWERS : Greenish-yellow, fragrant, small in ball-like clusters, 2–3cm. in diam. Jan.–Mar.

RUIT : Rounded, woody, about 2cm. in diam.

hroughout the deciduous forests of India.

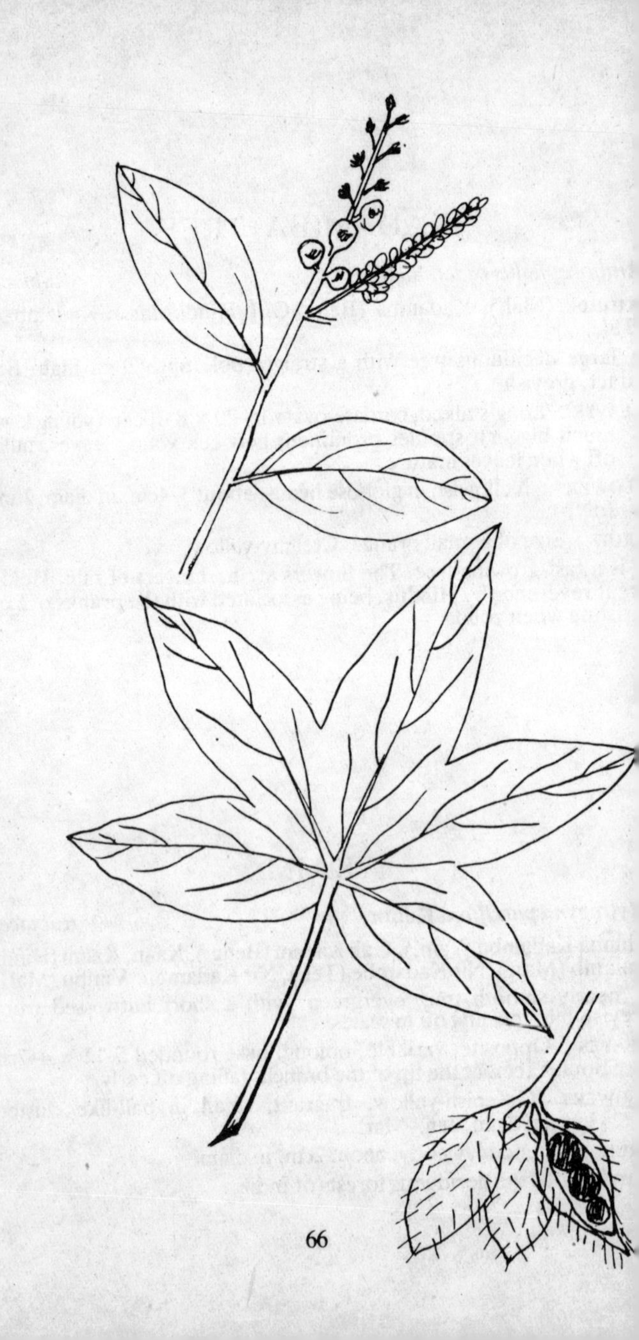

KAMALA

Mallotus philippensis Muell-Arg *Euphorbiaceae*

Kamala (Hindi/Beng.), Kapilo (Guj.), Kapli, Kungumam (Tam.), Kunkuma (Tel.), Manjana (Mal.), Shendri (Mar.)

A medium-sized, much branched, evergreen tree with a short bole, reaching upto 10m. Bark thin, grey, somewhat rough.

LEAVES : Alternate, simple, oval-oblong, variable, 8–12 × 6–8cm., smooth above, pubescent with numerous red glands beneath.

FLOWERS : Numerous, small, in spikes. Male and female on separate trees. Nov.–Jan.

FRUIT : Sub-globose, 3-lobed, 0.75–1.2cm. in diam. Densely covered with reddish-brown glandular pubescence. Seeds black, sub-globose.

Commonly occurs in scrub and mixed forests, ascending upto 1500m., as in the outer Himalayas. Widely distributed in North, Central, Western and Southern India. The coloured powder covering the fruits is used as a dye and possesses purgative properties.

KARAYA GUM

Sterculia urens Roxb. *Sterculiaceae*

Kagdol (Guj.), Karai (Guj./Mar.), Kavalam (Tam.), Kavili (Tel.), Kulu (Hindi).

A medium-sized, deciduous tree, upto 10m., with white or pinkish papery bark. When the tree is leafless in the cold season, the whitish bark gives it a grotesque appearance.

LEAVES : Large, 5-lobed, soft and velvety, 30–45cm., plate-like; stalk as long as leaf, stipules falling off early.

FLOWERS : Green or yellow with purple throat, star-shaped, strong-smelling and sticky, in clusters. Blooms where the tree is leafless in March–April.

FRUIT : 5 boat-shaped, woody fruitlets from one flower, looking like a starfish. Crimson-velvet when young. Woody-brown when old. Hairs bristly and stinging.

Common in most jungles. Indicative of rocky exposures. Often grows on rocky precipices. The seeds are liked by birds for their fleshy sweetish covering (aril).

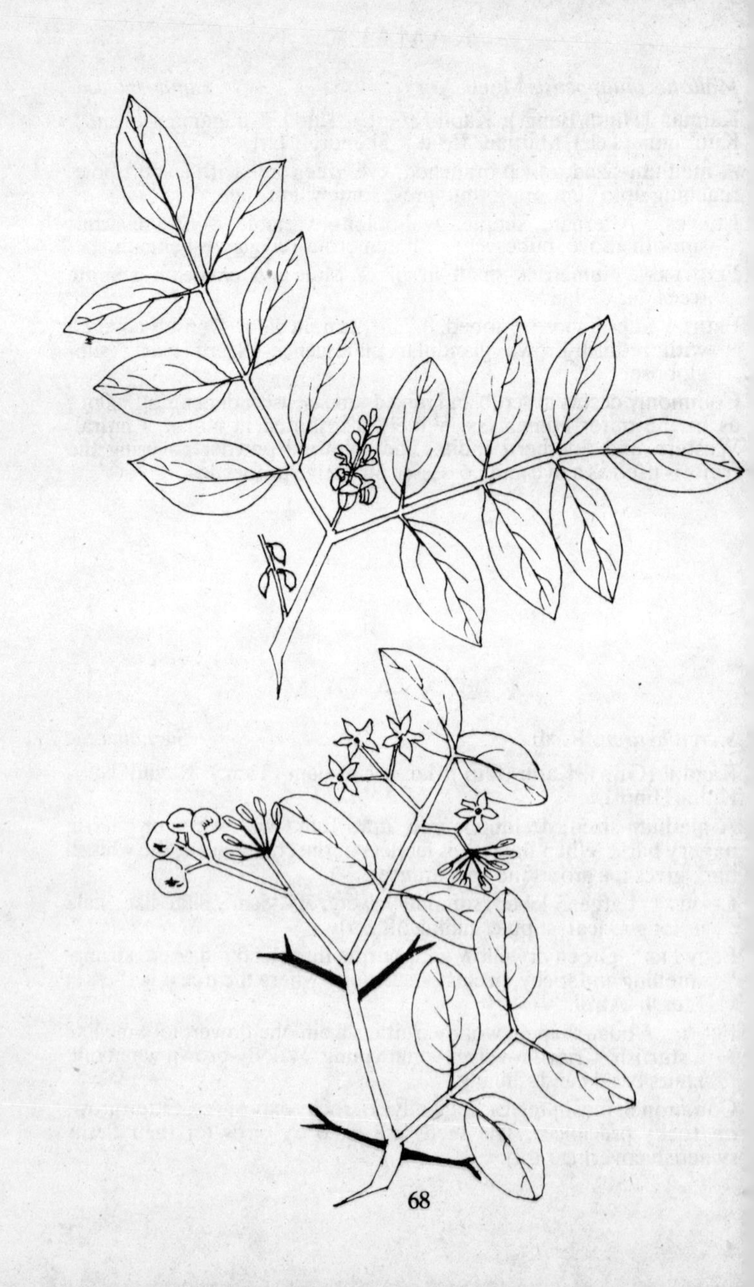

KARANJA

Pongamia pinnata Pierre
(= *P. glabra* Vent.) *Papilionaceae*

Karanj, Karanja (Hindi/Beng./Mar./Guj.), Ponga, Pongam (Tam.), Pungu (Mal./Tel.)

A moderate-sized, evergreen tree reaching upto 10–12m. Spreading crown with a short bole, covered by soft greyish-green bark, smooth or covered with tubercles.

LEAVES : Alternate, compound, imparipinnate, 5–7 leaflets, broadly elliptic, pale green with a pointed tip and peculiar bitterish smell when rubbed between fingers.

FLOWERS : White, tinged with pink or violet in axillary racemes, slightly fragrant. April–June. The fallen flowers form a mat under the tree early in the morning.

FRUIT : Compressed pod, woody when dry, ovate, tapering on both sides to sharp points. 1 seed.

A native of W. ghats, chiefly found along banks of streams and near coastal regions. Often cultivated as a shade tree alongside roads.

KARAUNDA

Carissa carandas Linn. *Apocynaceae*

Kalakkay (Tam.), Karamcha (Beng.), Karaunda (Hindi), Karvanda (Guj./Mar.), Karekayi (Kan.), Vaka (Tel.)

Rambling climber, often climbing on trees upto 20m. Milky. Branches with stout, straight twin thorns, often branched above.

LEAVES : Opposite, milky, elliptic, 3–8 × 2–5cm., smooth, shining.

FLOWERS : White 1–2cm., slightly fragrant in flat-topped clusters. Jan.–Apr.

FRUIT : Purplish black berries 1–2cm. in diam. Sticky, sweet, edible. Very common throughout dry, sandy and loamy soils in plains and low hills.

C. spinarum appears like the above but is usually cultivated for its more showy, pinkish, bigger fruit used to decorate women's hairdo.

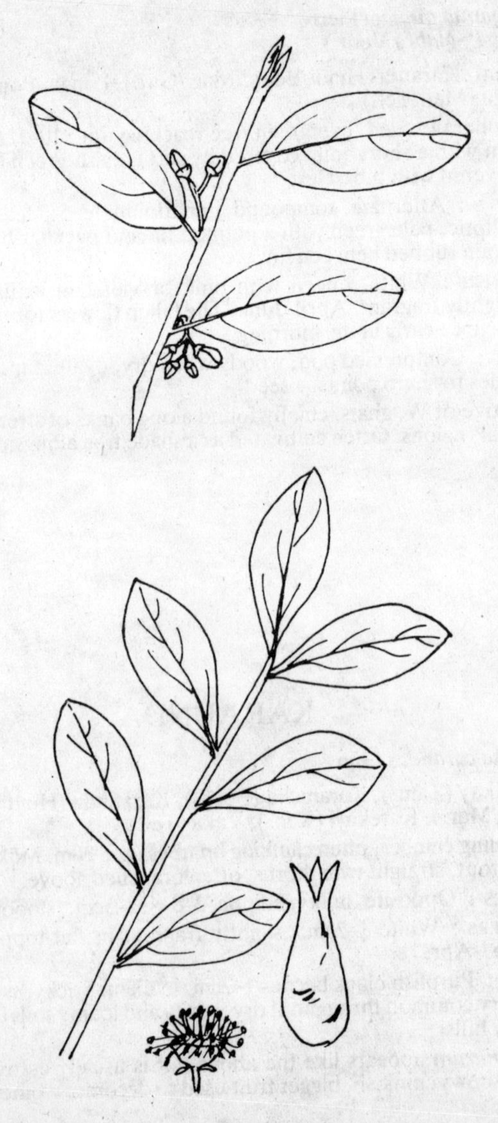

KHIRNI

Manilkara hexandra (Roxb.) Dubard *Sapotaceae*
(= *Mimusops hexandra* Roxb.)

Kirkhiyur (Beng.), Khirni (Hindi/Guj.), Pala (Tel.), Palla (Mal./Tam.), Rayan (Guj./Mar.)

A small, stiff tree, often reaching a great size with age; with a spreading crown and straight massive bole. Bark is dark-grey, deeply furrowed exuding drops of milky juice when hurt.

LEAVES : Elliptic to obovate, greyish-green, leathery, shiny 6–12 × 3.5–7cm., milky.

FLOWERS : Whitish or pale yellow, solitary or in axillary clusters. Sept.–Nov.

FRUIT : Yellow berry, ovoid 1.5–2cm., edible, sweet, sticky pulp.

Common in dry forests of W. India. The wood is useful. This species is used as a stock for grafting the *Achras sapota*—'chiku'—tree on it.

KUMBHI

Careya arborea Roxb. *Lecythidaceae*

Alam (Mal.), Araya (Tel.), Ayma (Tam.), Kumbi, Kumbhi (Hindi/Guj./Mar./Beng.)

A large handsome tree, more or less evergreen, reaching upto 20m. Trunk low, bearing a dense crown of large foliage on a round head. Bark dark-grey, thick, rough.

LEAVES : Alternate, stalkless, margin sparsely toothed, smooth, braodly ovate, leathery, 15–20 × 10–12cm.

FLOWERS : White, 8cm. across in thick clusters looking like big bottle-brushes. March–April.

FRUIT : Green, crowned with persistent sepals, globose, urnshaped, 6–7cm. in diam., smooth.

Common in deciduous and semi-evergreen forests all over the Indian plains.

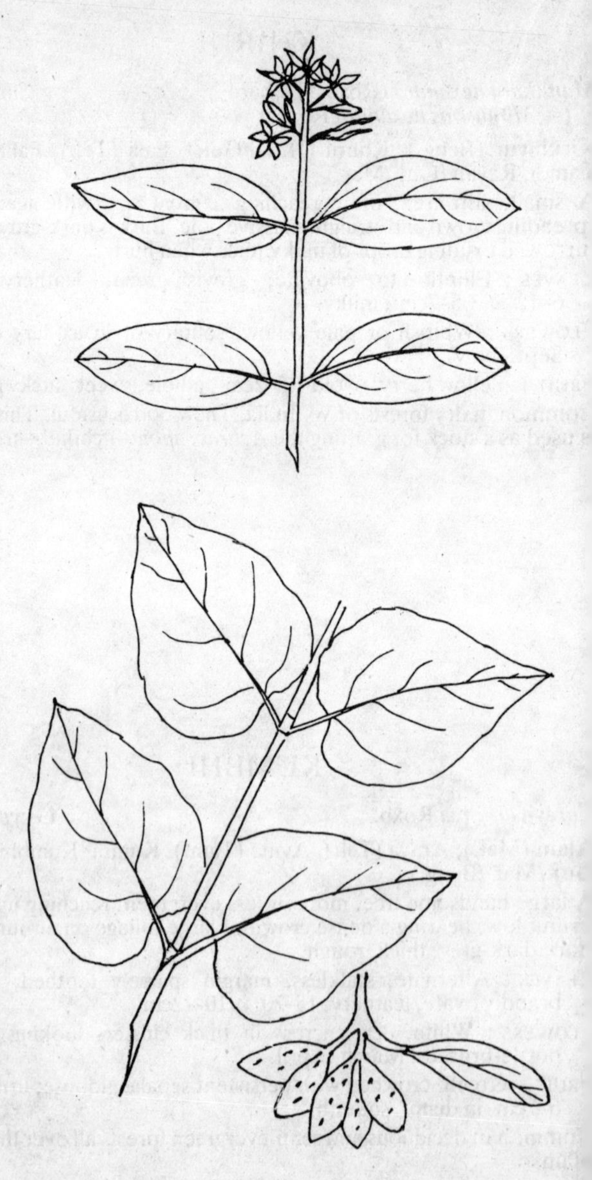

KURCHI/EASTER TREE

Hollarhena antidysenterica Wall. *Apocynaceae*

Kodaga (Tel.), Kuda (Guj./Mar.), Kurra, Kurchi (Hindi), Pala (Mal.), Veppalei (Tam.)

One of the commonest shrubs or small trees. Trunk and branches, rough, pale brown or grey, peeling in irregular flakes.

LEAVES : 15–30cm. long, opposing, milky, elliptic, about half as broad, on a small stalk.

FLOWERS : White, in flat-topped clusters, 15cm. in diam., not scented. Feb.-Aug.

FRUIT : In pairs, about 35–40cm. long, 1cm. in diam. with whitish spots.

Common in deciduous forests. Kurchi bark is the source of an important medicine for dysentery. The seeds are also similarly used in indigenous medicament. The tree is in full bloom at Easter. The flowers lend themselves to the decoration of Churches for the festival, giving the tree its adopted name.

KUTHAN (Trade)

Hymenodictyon excelsum Wall. *Rubiaceae*

Bandarayanni (Kan.), Bhamarchhal (Guj.), Dandelo (Mar.), Lati Karum (Beng.), Vella Katampu (Mal.), Vellei Kadambu (Tam.)

A tall tree 10–15m. high, trunk straight, bark smooth, branches ascending.

LEAVES : Opposite, membraneous, 10–15 × 7–10cm., ovate-elliptic, abruptly long tip base narrows into the stalk, pubescent on both sides.

FLOWERS : Numerous, greenish-white, fragrant, in terminal clusters. June–Aug.

FRUIT : A capsule 2cm. long, ellipsoid.

Frequent in *ghat* jungles, and deciduous forests.

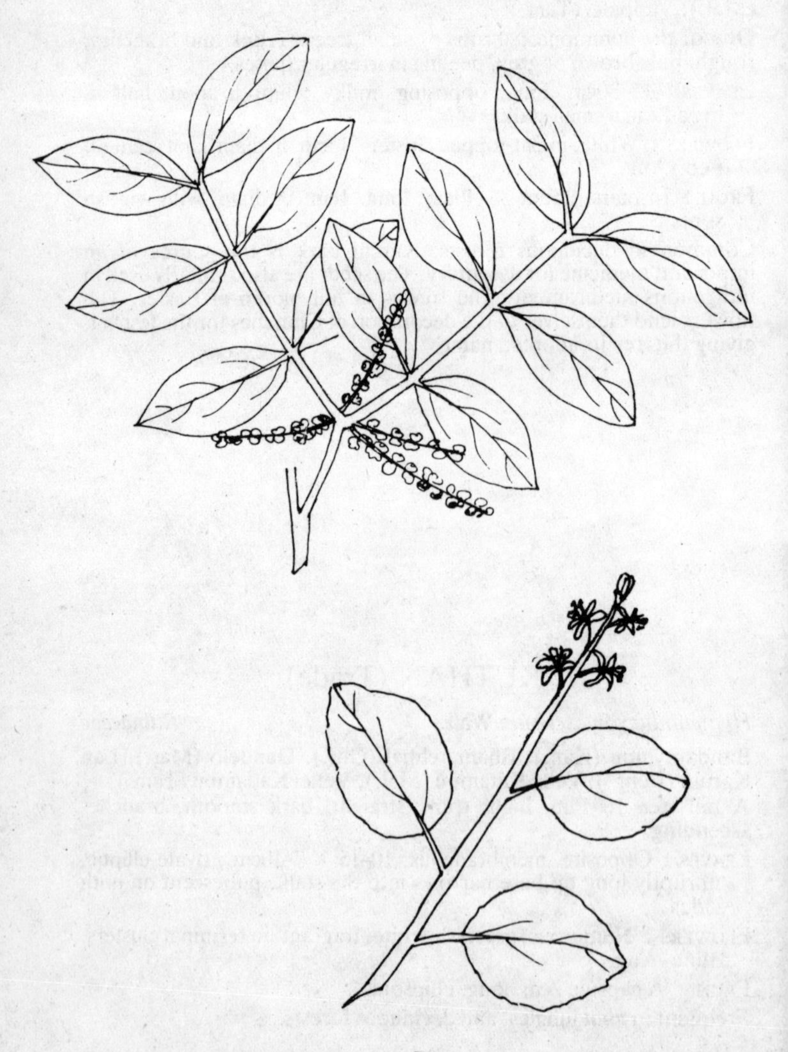

THE LAC TREE

Schleichera oleosa (Lour.) Oken. *Sapindaceae*
(= *s. trijnga* Willd.)

Kusum (Hindi, Beng., Mar., Guj.), Posuku (Tel.), Puvam (Mal.), Puvathipuvam (Tam.)

A medium-sized to large tree upto 30m. in height, nearly evergreen; grey, flaky bark, reddish inside.

LEAVES : Paripinnate, with 6 leaflets (sometimes 8). Leaflets elliptic, rough 5–25 × 3–10cm. New leaves reddish.

FLOWERS : Small, yellowish-green in bunches, male and bisexual; popular with honey-bees. April–May.

FRUIT : Globose or ovoid berries with blunt prickles, upto 2cm. long and 1.5cm. in diam. with 1–2 oily seeds.

Occurs in mixed deciduous forests all over India, and harbours lac insects. When in new leaf, the tree sets the forest alight with fiery copper-coloured crown or bunches of leaves at the end of branches.

LASORA

Cordia dichotoma Forsk. *Boraginaceae*
(= *c. myxa* Roxb.
= *c. obliqua* Willd.)

Bahubare (Beng.), Bhokar (Mar.), China makkeru (Tel.), Gunda (Guj.), Lasora (Hindi), Naruvili (Tam.), Verasham, Vidi, Veri (Mal.)

A moderate sized tree with usually crooked trunk and large fissured bark, upto 10m. high.

LEAVES : Alternate, broadly ovate, obtuse, variable in shape, entire or slightly dentate, more or less rough above, base rounded or cordate, three basal nerves. Stalk 2–4 cm. long.

FLOWERS : Small, white in terminal clusters, profuse. March–April.

FRUIT : Globose about 3cm. in diam., green at first turning pinkish-cream or turning black on ripening. It is held on a saucer shaped calyx and contains copious mucilage and a very hard stony seed. The fruit is sweet to taste and edible, and can be pickled.

Distributed in all the warmer parts of the Indian subcontinent, seen near river banks, *nullahs* and upto 300m. alt. It is often cultivated for its fruit on marginal land.

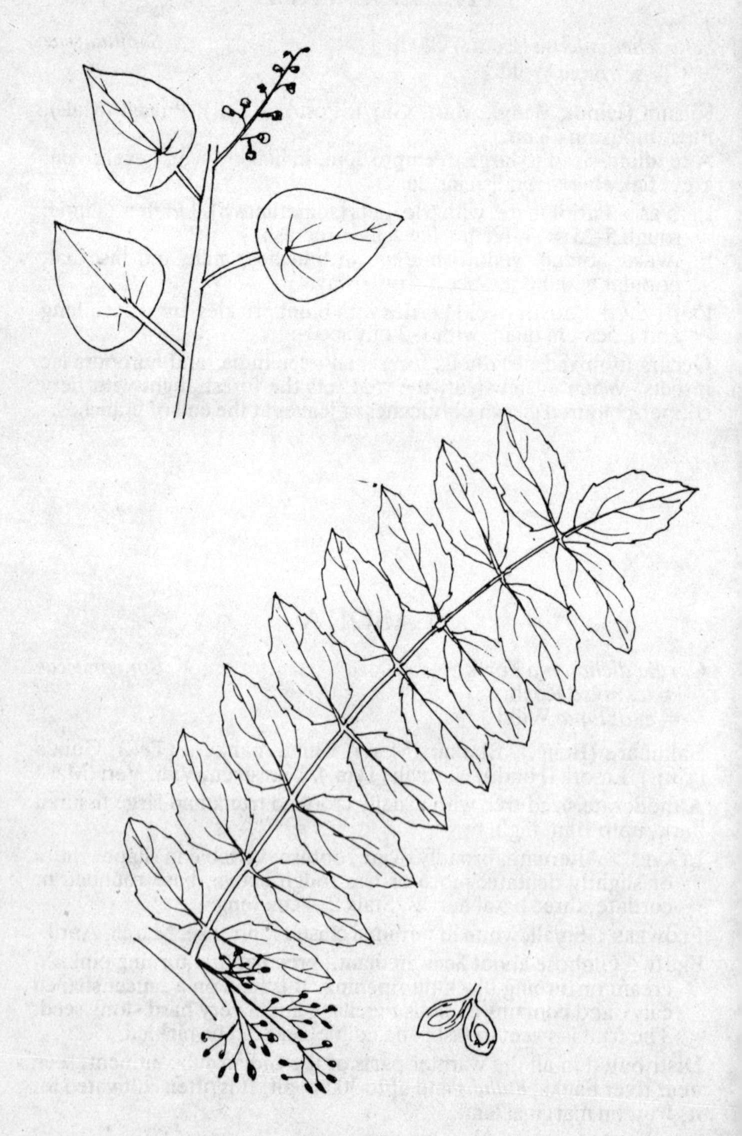

MACARANGA

Macaranga tomentosa Wt. *Euphorbiaceae*
(= *M. peltata* Mull-Arg.)

Boddi (Tel.), Chanda (Mar.), Uppila (Mal.), Vattakanni (Tam.)

A medium-sized evergreen tree, upto 10m. high with a low trunk and rounded crown. Bark dark-grey. Branches stout, young shoots tomentose.

LEAVES : 10–20 × 8–14cm., orbicular, broadly toothed, smooth above, pubescent below, gland dotted, stalk 8–15cm. holding the blade like an umbrella (peltate), stipules falling off early.

FLOWERS : Male and female on the same tree. Male—minute in dense heads, covered by bracts. Female flowers larger, also enclosed in bracts. Jan.–March.

FRUIT : Globose, about 1cm. in diam., hairy and glandular.

Common in deciduous forests.

MAHARUK (MAHANIMB)

Ailanthus excelsa Roxb. *Simaroubaceae*

Arduso (Guj.), Doddmara (Kan.), Maharuk (Hindi, Mar.), Peddamanu (Tel.), Perumaram (Tam.)

A large deciduous tree upto 30m. in height, with light grey intact bark.

LEAVES : Imparipinnate, 25–50cm. long with 8–14 pairs of leaflets which are very variable in shape. Each leaflet 10–15 × 3–4cm., lance-shaped, neem-like, serrate, oblique at base. Smell bitterish.

FLOWERS : Small and yellowish in large lax bunches. April–May.

FRUIT: Flat pod-like, brown, winged 3–5 × 1cm., tapering at both ends; twisted at base.

A graceful tree occuring in deciduous forests; often planted on roadsides.

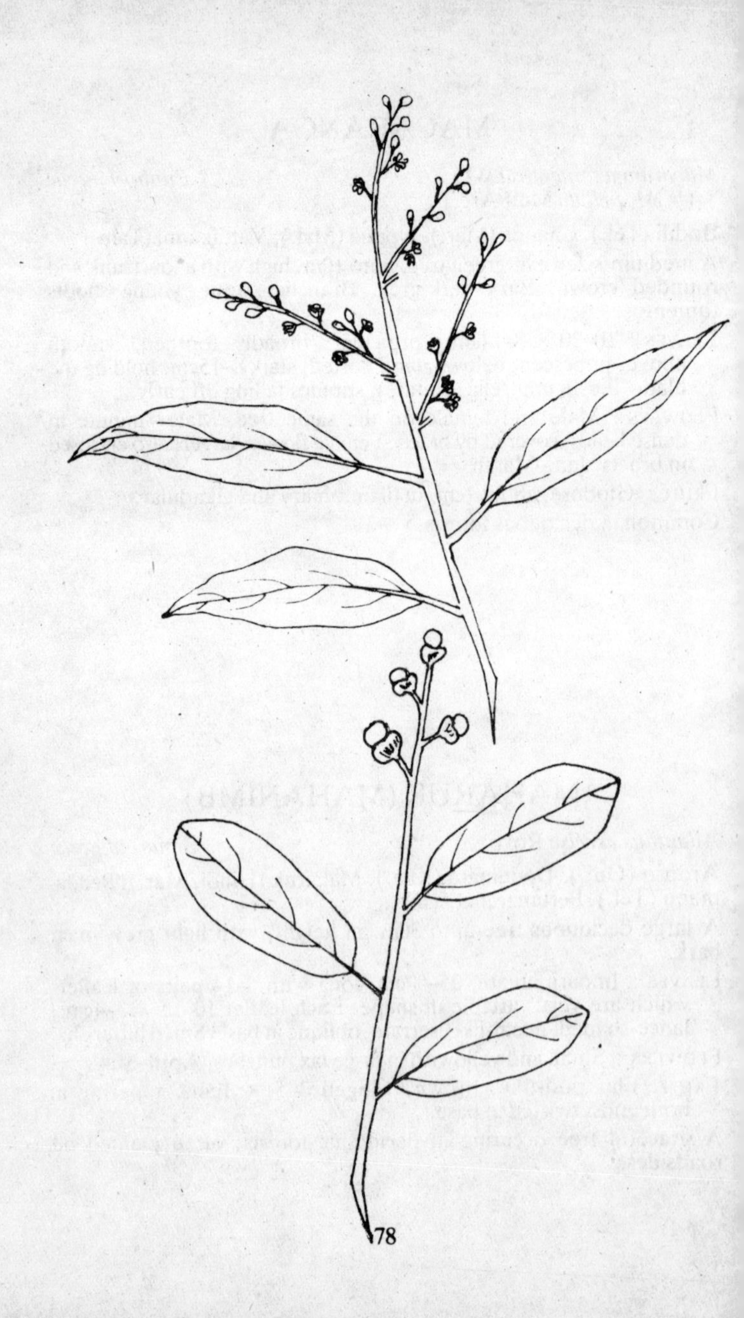

MANGO

Mangifera indica Linn. *Anacardiaceae*

Am (Hindi/Beng.), Amba (Guj./Mar.), Amram (Mal.), Mamidi (Tel.), Manga (Tam.)

A large evergreen tree with a dense dome-shaped crown of leaves, reaching upto 20m. Trunk straight, stout with dark-grey rough bark, cracking when old.

LEAVES : Crowded at the ends of branches, oblong-lanceolate, 8–25 × 4–8cm. Shining, margin entire to wavy.

FLOWERS : Yellowish-white, small in dense clusters, larger than leaves, fragrant. Jan.–March.

FRUIT : Large, fleshy, sub-ovoid 8–15cm. long. April–June.

Wild in mixed deciduous forests but mainly culvitated for its luscious fruit both by farmers and householders. Considered an auspicious tree.

THE MARKING NUT TREE

Semecarpus anacardium Linn. f. *Anacardiaceae*

Bhallataki (Tam.), Bhela, Bhilawa (Hindi), Bhilataki (Beng.), Bibba, Bhilawa (Guj./Mar.), Chera (Mal.), Shen kottai (Tam.)

A moderate sized deciduous tree upto 12–15m. high. Trunk dark brown, rough.

LEAVES : Alternate, simple, oblong or ovate, whitish, 17–60 × 10–30cm. clustered near the ends of branches, strongly veined below. Leafless in Feb.–April.

FLOWERS : In long terminal clusters. May–August.

FRUIT : Drupes, 2–5cm. long, obliquely ovoid, somewhat flattened, smooth, shining, black when ripe, situated on a fleshy orange-coloured, soft peduncle which is edible but astringent. The rind of the hard nut abounds in an oil which is bitter and turns black and is highly blistering (allergic to skin). This juice of the fruit is traditionally used for marking linen by Indian washermen and also used now for the varnish paint and plastic industry. The inner flesh is edible.

Fairly common throughout the hotter parts of India in the deciduous forests.

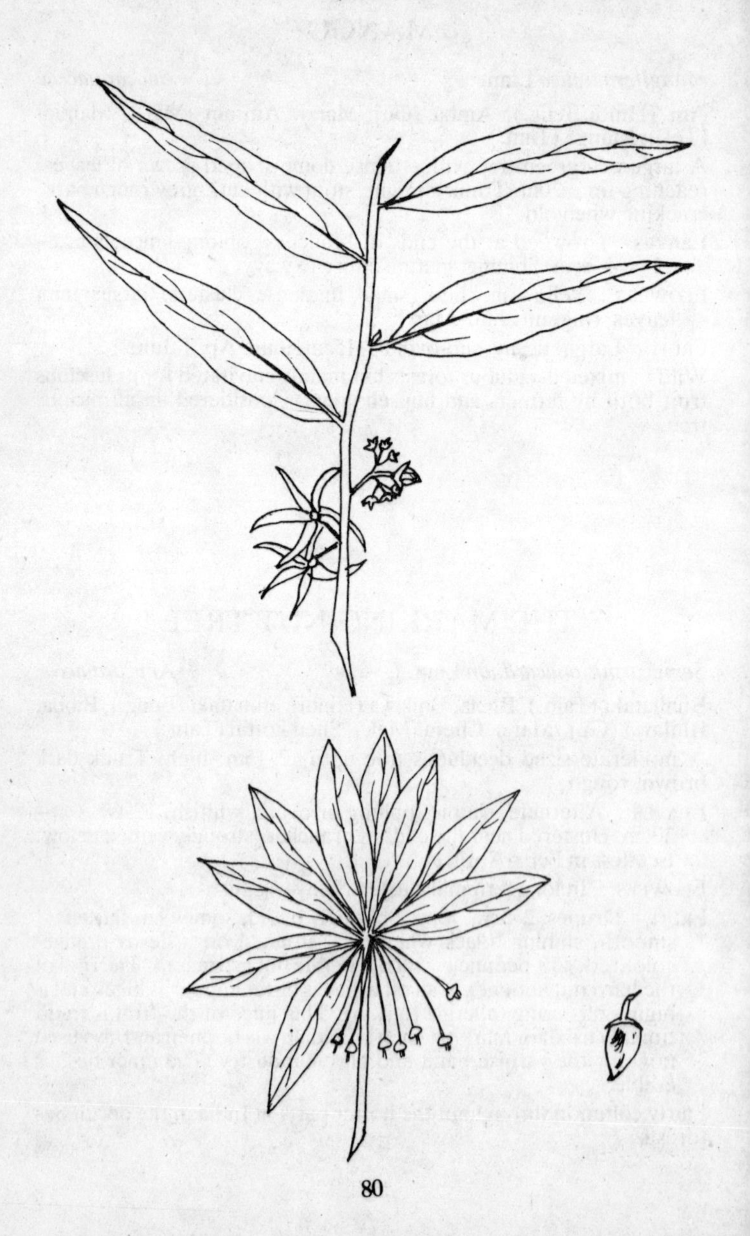

MAST TREE

Polyalthia longifolia Thev. *Annonaceae*

Arana (mal.), Asoka (Hindi/Mar.), Asopalav (Guj.), Assothe (Tam.), Deb daru (Beng.), Nana meamidi (Tel.), Nettilingam (Tam.)

A tall, evergreen tree about 20–25m. high. Trunk straight, bark smooth, greyish-brown. Variety 'pendula' has markedly drooping branches.

LEAVES : Glossy-green, lance-shaped with wavy margin, dotted with translucent oil glands.

FLOWERS : Inconspicuous, greenish in bunches of 5–6. Feb.–April.

FRUIT : Globular to ovoid, green, abundant, containing a ringed seed which germinates readily. Fruits relished by birds, bats and squirrels.

Cultivated as an ornamental or avenue tree in gardens and on roadsides. Also considered sacred and often planted near temples. The leaves are used in wreaths on festive occasions.

MOHWA

Madhuca indica Gmel. *Sapotaceae*
(*M. latifoliae* Macb.
= *Bassia latifolia* Roxb.)

Illupei (Tam.), Ippa (Tel.), Mahua, Mahwa (Beng./Guj./Hindi/Mar.), Poonam (Mal.)

A deciduous, medium-sized tree upto 15m. Trunk with a short bole and numerous branches forming a thick leafy crown. Bark dark-coloured, cracked, exuding milky latex.

LEAVES : Clustered near the ends of branches, leathery, elliptic, hairy when young, 10–20 × 5–13cm. Coppery brown when tender.

FLOWERS : Pendulous in dense clusters at the ends of branches, calyx rusty, corolla creamy, fleshy, edible, sweet. A good tree may yield 200 kg. of petals per year.

FRUIT : Fleshy, ovoid berry, densely rusty, 4–5cm. in diam., 1–4 seeds.

Common throughout the Indian plains, particularly in M.P. Often cultivated near *adivasi* habitations, both for flowers and seeds which are rich in oil.

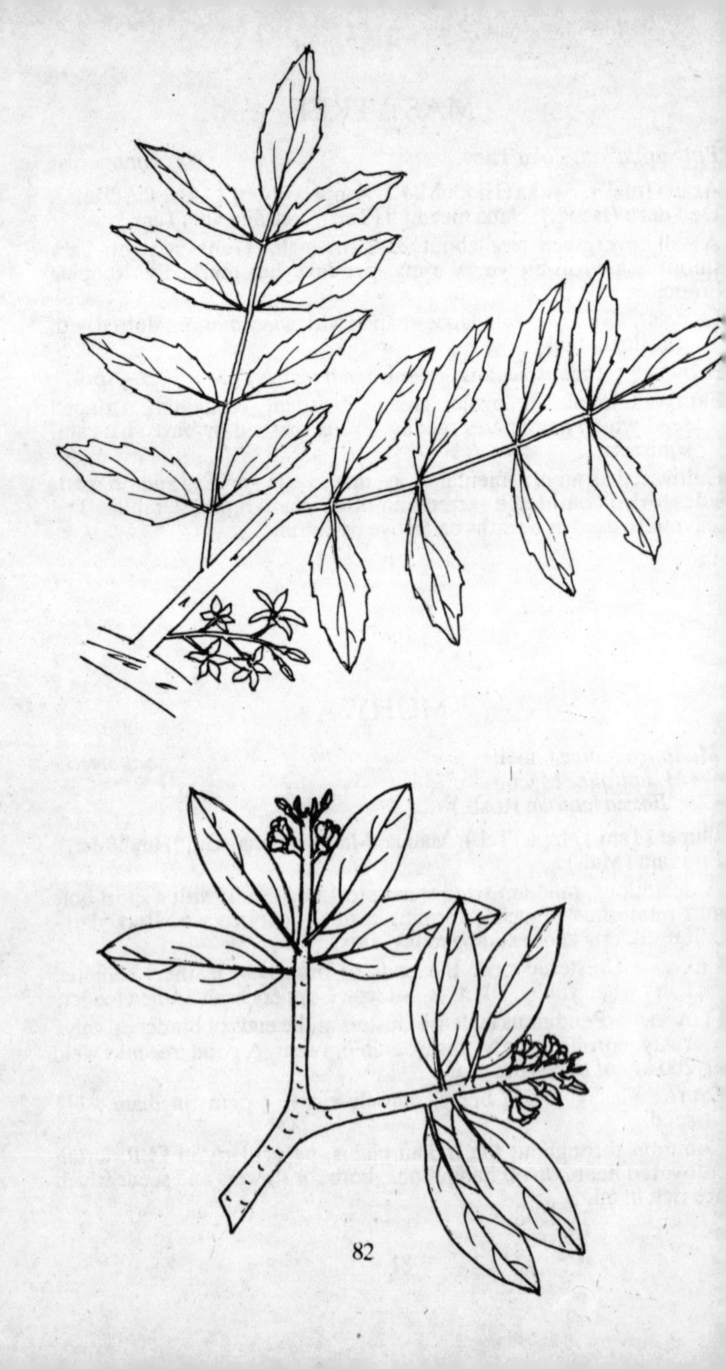

NEEM / MARGOSA

Azadirachta indica A. Juss. *Meliaceae*

Limdo (Guj.), Neem (Hindi/Beng.), Vepa (Mal./Tam./Tel.)

One of the best-known and important Indian trees. Large, evergreen tree upto 15m. tall. Bark dark grey, with long and oblique fissures on the outer surface.

LEAVES : Alternate, imparipinnate (odd number of leaflets). Each leaflet oblique, lanceolate with toothed margin, slightly curved, bitter in taste.

FLOWERS : Whitish, honey-scented, small in axillary panicles. Attract a large number of bees.

FRUIT : Greenish-yellow, 1.5 × 1cm., egg-like, oval, 1-seeded. Relished by birds.

This is one of the commonest trees in India, though a native of Burma. It is considered a sacred and health-giving tree chiefly because of its insecticidal and medicinal properties. Deep rooted, it is specially suitable for dry climate and semi-desert or scrub land. A slightly bitterish gum exudes from old trunks.

PAGODA TREE

Plumeria rubra Linn. *Apocynaceae*

Arali (Tam.), Champa (Guj./Mar.), Ezha champakam (Mal.), Garuda champa (Beng.), Golainchi (Hindi), Kathali champa (Beng.), Khair champa (Mar.), Nuruvarahalu (Tel.)

A small gouty-looking tree which is often leafless but rarely out of bloom.

> 'Rough and uncouth thy form
> Steadfast before the storm
> Pointing to heaven from the graves of
> the dead.'
>
> (From Waterfield's Eulogy)[10]

LEAVES : Grow in crowded 'spirals' at the tips of the branches exceeding 30cm., smooth, broadly lance-shaped, tapering at both ends. Veins are distinctive and straight. Leaves fall off during Nov.–Dec., only reappearing with the next rains.

FLOWERS : In upright clusters at the tips of branches, white and pink varieties are common, fragrant. Feb.–Oct.

FRUIT : Pods in pairs, about 12cm. long.

A native of Jamaica, is established throughout the warm parts of India. Cultivated as an ornamental tree or as a floral offering near graves.

P. alba is another very graceful tree with pure white, fragrant flowers.

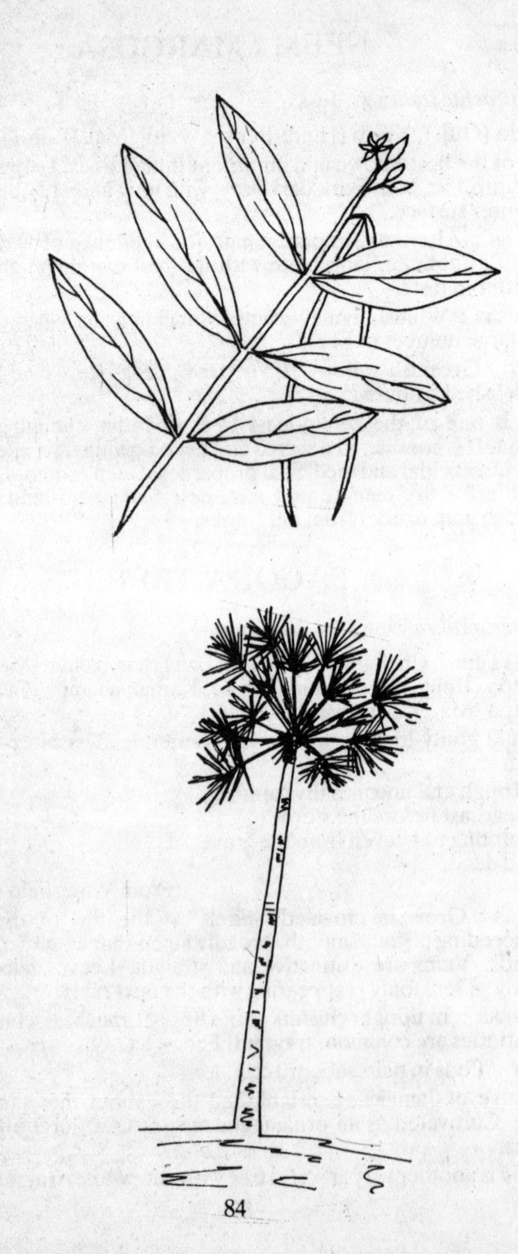

PALA INDIGO

Wrightia tinctoria R. Br. *Apocynaceae*

Dudhlo (Guj.), Indrajav (Beng./Hindi), Kala kuda (Mar.), Kotaka palla (Mal.), Mitho indrajav (Guj.), Tedlapaala (Tel.), Veypale (Tam.)

A pretty small tree upto 7m. high. Trunk and branches irregularly shaped, smooth, scaly bark.

LEAVES : Opposite, milky, several times longer than broad, 7–15 × 3–6cm., smooth.

FLOWERS : White, fragrant, in loose terminal clusters. Petals with a fringe, almost like double petals. March–May.

FRUIT : A pair of drooping, green, cylindrical pod-like fruit, 25–50cm. long, united at the tip.

Common in deciduous forests all over India.

An allied tree *W. tomentosa*, has fruit in which the pair of pod-like fruits are attached or united forming one long jointed thick pod covered with brown specks.

PALMYRA PALM

Borassus flabellifer Linn. *Arecaceae*

Pana (Mal.), Panai (Tam.), Tad (Guj.), Tal, Tar (Hindi/Beng.), Tadi chettu (Tel.)

A tall, unbranched palm reaching upto 40m. in height and 60cm. in diam. Straight, black stem. Younger trees are covered with dead leaves, or bases of stalks. Base of the stem bears rootless.

LEAVES : Simple, palmate, 1–2m. in diam., with stout curved stalks upto 1m. arranged in a terminal crown of 30–40 large fan-like leaves.

FLOWERS : Male and female flowers are borne on different trees. Female spikes are larger, covered by a boat-shaped spathe (special type of leaf). Male flowers minute, embedded in fleshy axes, each about 30cm., cylindrical, 3–4cm. in diam., arising from a spathe.

FRUIT : A globose drupe upto 20cm. in diam. with fleshy transparent pulp with 1 seed chamber.

Native of Tropical Africa, cultivated in India in low sandy areas proximate to coastal regions. Leaves used for thatching huts.

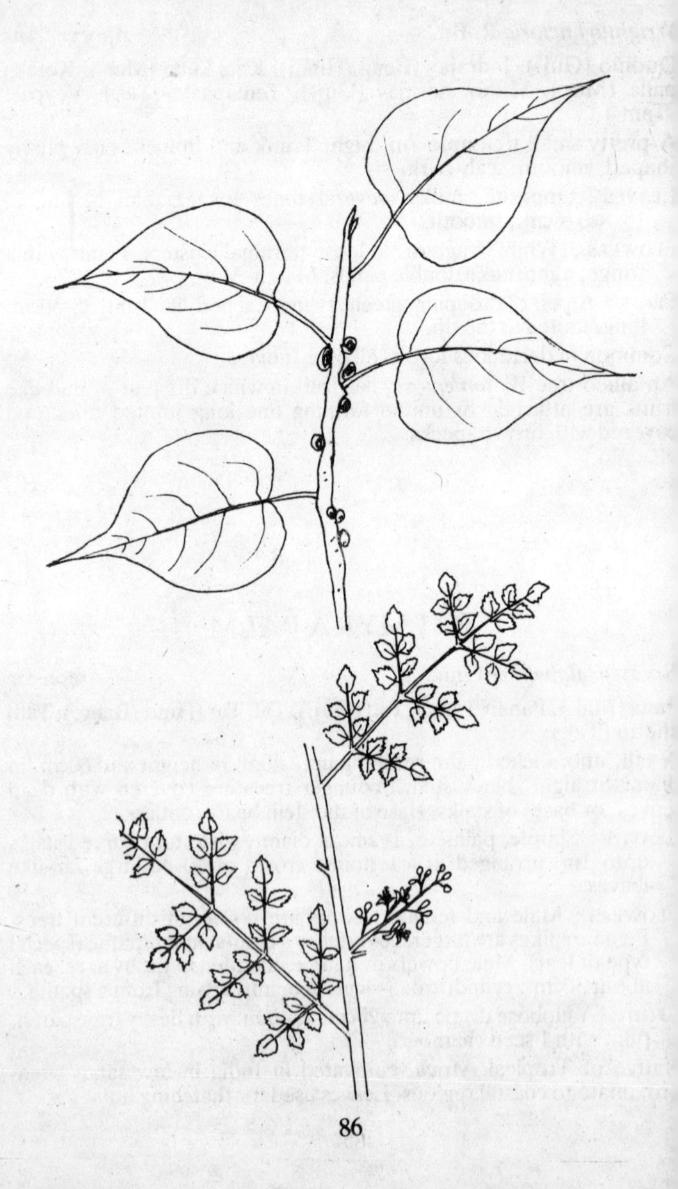

PEEPAL

Ficus religiosa Linn. *Moraceae*

Arachu (Mal.), Ashvatham (Beng./Mal./Tam.), Pimpal (Mar.), Pipal (Hindi), Piplo (Guj.)

The sacred tree of the Hindus often occurs as an epiphyte on palm trees, on rocks, precipitous hills and walls (dispersal by birds). Normally it grows upto 15m. with a smooth, handsome trunk with fibrous aerial roots.

LEAVES : Alternate, heart-shaped on a long stalk and often in perpetual motion in the breeze are pleasing to the eye and the ear — 'restless as the leaves of the tall poplar tree' ('Odyssey').[11] The bud is covered by stipules which often elongate and turn pinkish.

FLOWERS : Are borne inside the tender figs which are haunted by tiny insects.

FRUIT : The figs when ripe are relished by birds who excrete the seeds that germinate on old walls and precipitous rocks.

A common tree all over India, and one of great antiquity. A Kew record gives the age of a tree at Anuragapura in 1852 to be 2147 years old. (Nairne).[12]

PERSIAN LILAC

Melia azedarach Linn. *Meliaceae*

Bakain (Hindi), Bakan limbdo (Guj.), Karin vembu (Mal.), Malai vembu (Tam.), Pejri (Mar.), Turaka vepa (Tel.)

A fast-growing, moderate-sized, tree upto 13m. tall. Cylindrical bole with wide spreading branches covered by greyish-brown bark, marked with long shallow vertical fissures.

LEAVES : Alternate, bi-tripinnate, bright green. Leaflets lance-shaped with toothed margin 7–8 × 2cm., leaf base unequal sided. Occasionally the leaves are shed.

FLOWERS : Lilac, honey-scented in long, axillary panicles about 18–20cm. long. Feb.–March; occasionally flowers in Dec.

FRUIT: Fleshy, globular, about 1–1.5cm. in diam., with 4 tiny seeds in a hard shell.

Indigenous to Baluchistan, but naturalized all over India and many tropical countries. Several forms of the tree are reported varying in size and flower colour.

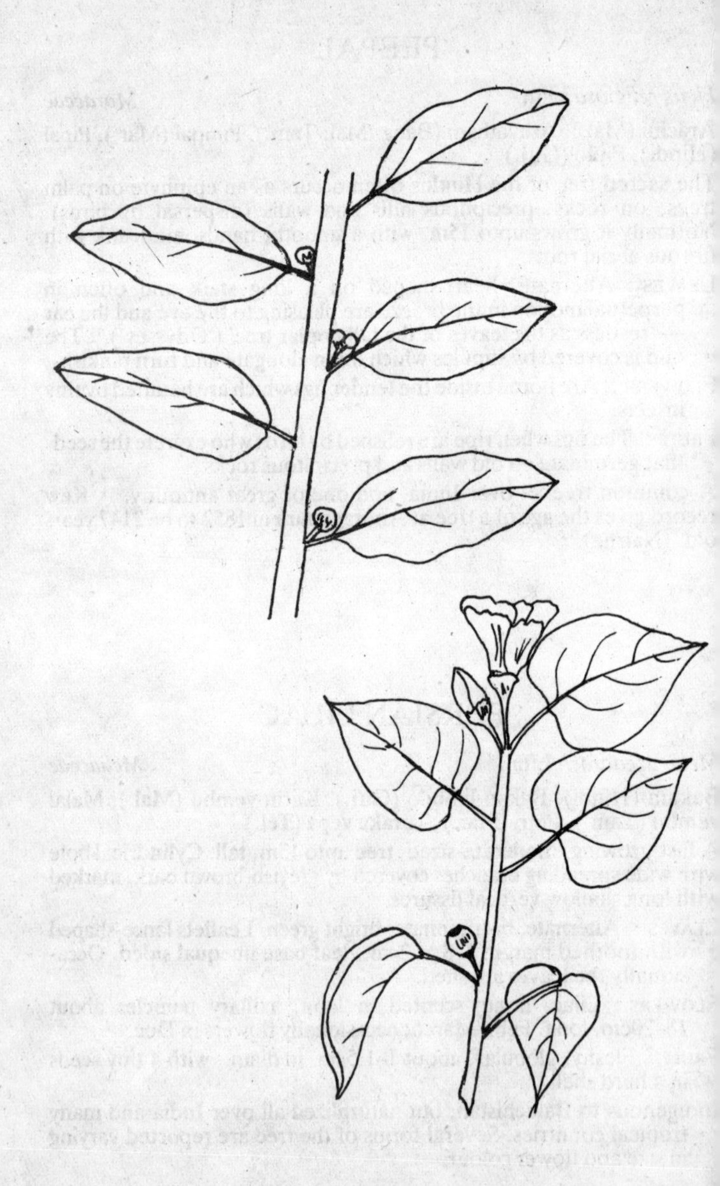

PILU (KHAKAN – Trade)

Salvadora persica Linn. *Salvadoraceae*

Jhal (Hindi/Beng.), Kalwa (Tam.), Khakhin (Mar.), Pilu (Guj.)

A large, much branched evergreen tree; bark dull-grey or grey-white, deeply cracked, young branches almost white.

LEAVES : Opposite, elliptic-ovate or ovate lanceolate, rather variable in shape, fleshy, veins scarcely visible

FLOWERS : Very small greenish-white or yellowish in lax panicles. Nov.–May.

FRUIT: Globose, about 3–4mm. in diam., red when ripe, sweet, edible. Seed yields a yellowish non-edible oil used sometimes in local medicine and soap-making.

Found in dry and arid regions of India and on saline lands and in coastal regions. Often called the *Mustard tree* of the scripture:

'..... the mustard tree
that hath seed so little and its boughs
wide spreading.'
(Arnold)[13].

Salvadora olioides Decne is a smaller tree with narrower leaves found in the drier regions of Northern India. Yields a similar oil from seeds sold as 'Khakan' oil in commerce.

PORTIA TREE

Thespesia populnea Soland. *Malvaceae*

Bhendi (Mar.), Gangaraavi (Tel.), Paras pipal (Hindi/Guj./Beng.), Poovarasu (Mal.), Poovarasam Kallai (Tam.)

A small to medium-sized evergreen tree 10–15m. high, trunk straight with greyish fissured bark, branches closely set forming a dense crown.

LEAVES : Broad, heart-shaped with a pointed tip, 7–15 × 10cm., dark green, flecked beneath with minute rusty scales.

FLOWERS : Yellow with a purple centre, completely changing to orange when about to wither, 8–10mm. across, almost throughout the year.

FRUIT : Globular, turban-shaped, cupped by calyx with minute, numerous, seeds.

Grows wild along beaches and tidal forests of coastal regions. Often planted in gardens and on roadsides for its shade-giving character.

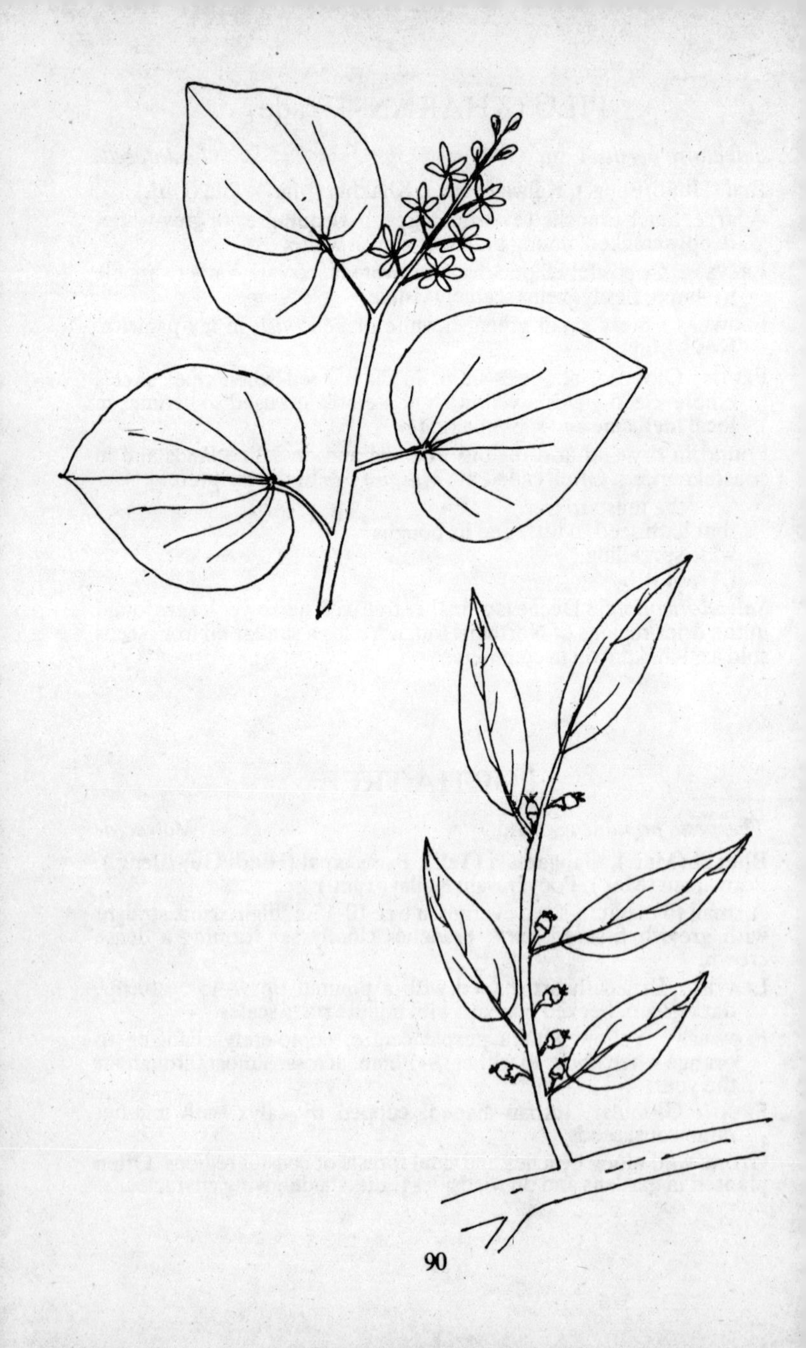

PULA

Kydia calycina Roxb. *Malvaceae*

Moti hiravani (Guj.), Pola (Beng.), Pula (Hindi), Potri (Tel.), Velukku (Mal.), Vendai (Tam.)

Rapidly growing medium-sized deciduous tree upto 12m. high. Trunk with greyish bark exfoliating in irregular flakes of long strips.

LEAVES : Alternate, with 5 nerves arising from the base, lobed, base heart-shaped, closely felted beneath, 10–12 × 8–10cm. with a pointed tip.

FLOWERS : Greenish-white to purplish in much branched panicles, clothed with dense tomentum. Sept.–Nov.

FRUIT : 3-valved capsule, size of a pea enveloped by an enlarged calyx containing kidney-shaped seeds.

Common in mixed deciduous forests all over India and the sub-Himalayan region.

PUTRANJIVA

Putranjiva roxburghii Wall. *Euphorbiaceae*

Irukolli (Tam.), Kudrajivi (Tel.), Pongalam (Mal.), Putajan (Mar.), Putranjiva (Hindi/Beng./Guj.)

An evergreen tree upto 10–15m. high, branches drooping like the willow; bark grey, corky; young shoots tomentose.

LEAVES : Alternate, shining, leathery, linear-oblong, 8–10cm., margin wavy, stipules pubescent, 1mm.

FLOWERS : Male and female on different trees: male small in dense rounded clusters, yellowish; female flowers solitary or, in groups of 2–3, greenish. March–May & July–Nov.

FRUIT : Rounded, indistinctly 3-lobed, greenish-grey about 1.5cm. in diam. with 1 seed.

The tree sometimes occurs in deciduous forests, but is more often cultivated for its gracefully falling branches and evergreen habit. Considered useful in indigenous medicine.

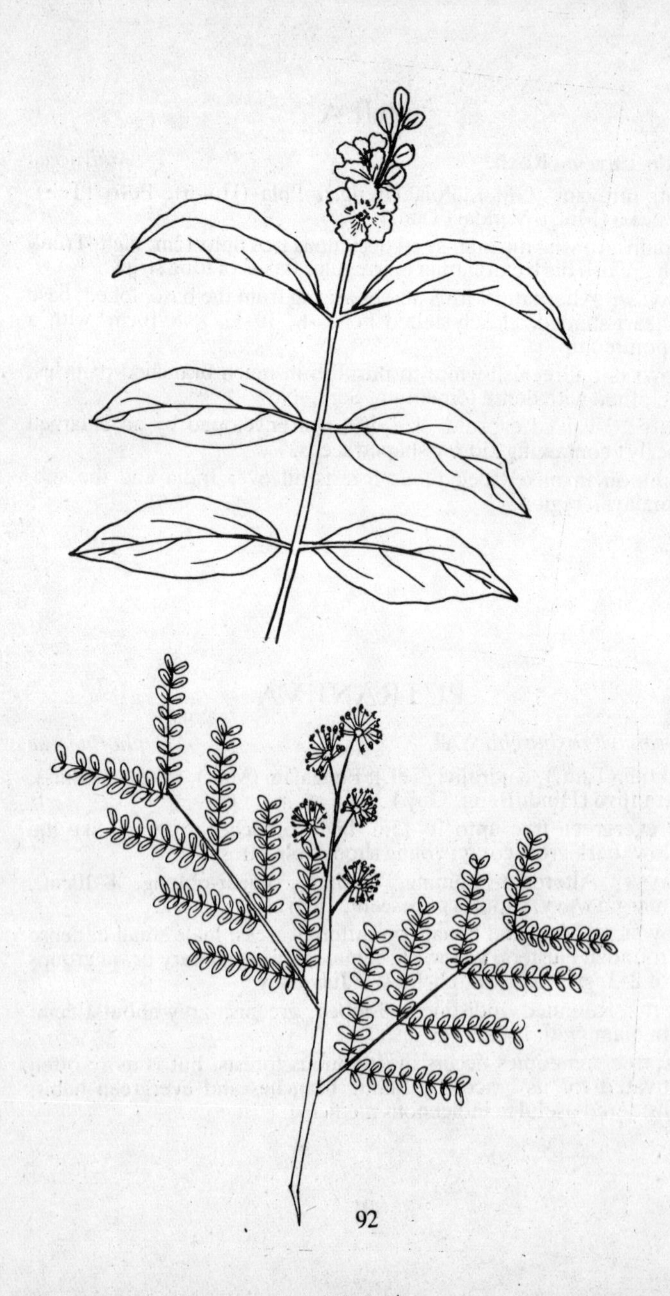

QUEEN'S FLOWER

Lagerstroemia speciosa Pers. *Lythraceae*
(= *L. flos-reginae* Retz.)

Jarool, Jarul (Hindi, Beng.), Kadali (Tam.), Marumaruthu (Mal.), Taman (Mar.)

A medium-sized deciduous tree with a rounded crown. Bark smooth, greyish, exfoliating in irregular flakes.

LEAVES : Opposite, oblong-lanceolate, elliptic, smooth, 15 × 5cm.

FLOWERS : In large panicles, mauve to purple. June-July.

FRUIT : Capsules ellipsoid or sub-globose, about 25cm. in diam. with 3–4 seeds.

It is a well-known ornamental tree and is widely cultivated in gardens and on road-sides.

RAIN TREE

Enterolobium saman Prain *Mimosaceae*
(= *Samanea saman* Merrill
= *Pithecellobium saman* Benth.)

Belati siris, Koroi (Beng.), Nidraganneru (Tel.), Thunga moonji (Tam.), Vilayti siris (Guj./Mar.)

A large deciduous tree of great size, reaching upto 15m. in height and 20–25m. in the diameter of its crown. Thick short bole covered by dark grey bark with vertical cracks.

LEAVES : Bipinnate, dark green upto 35cm. long. Pinnae upto 20cm. long the outermost largest. Leaflets 8–10 pairs, opposite, oblique, ovate-oblong, obtuse about 3 × 2cm. Leaves are shed early in the cold season and the tree is leafless for a short time.

FLOWERS : In globose heads upto 5cm. in diam., on long stalks (10–12cm.), yellowish petals with long, pink, silky stamens. March-Oct. following the flush of new leaves.

FRUIT : Pods, straight upto 20cm. × 2–3cm.; slightly flattened, smooth.

A native of Brazil, cultivated as an ornamental tree. Grows comparatively rapidly. The English name orginated from its often being infected by insects which discharge small drops of water which was taken to be discharge of rain from the tree—hence, Rain Tree.

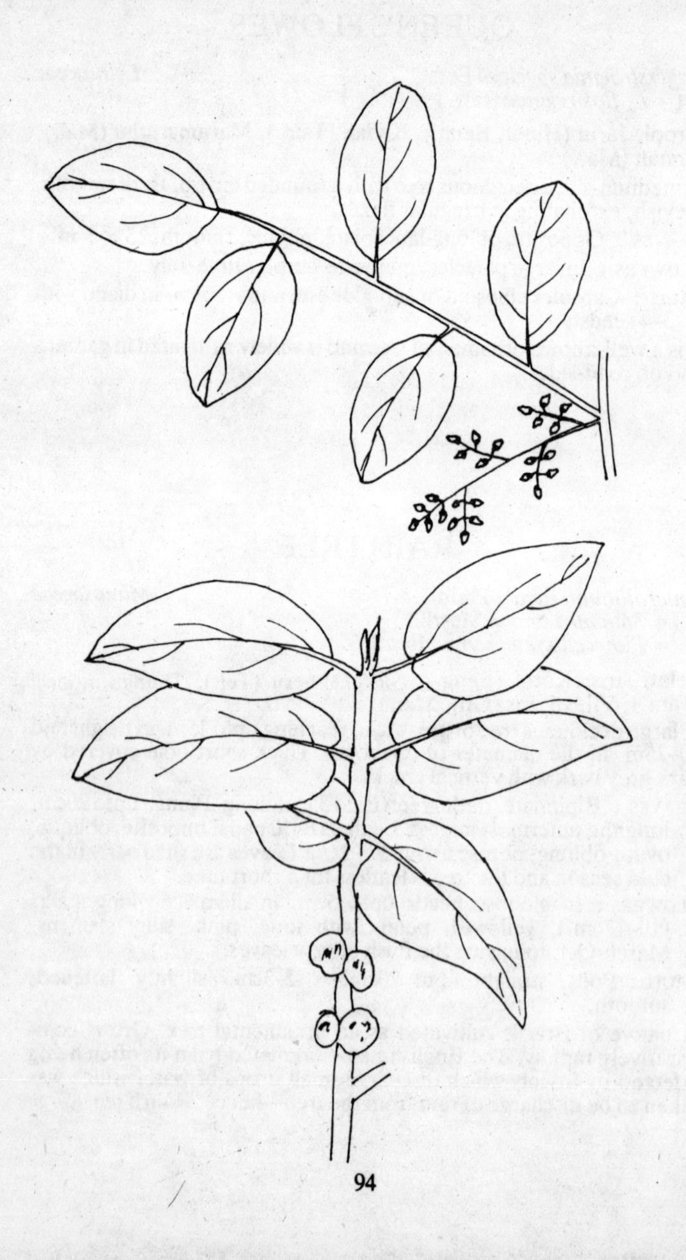

ROSEWOOD

Dalbergia latifolia Roxb. *Papilionaceae*

Cittegi (Tel.), Itti (Mal./Tam.), Shisham (Hindi/Guj./Mar.), Sitsal (Beng.)

A tall, straight, deciduous tree, upto 20m. high. In northern India, it tends to assume the form of a low, branching tree. The greyish bark is marked with short irregular cracks and peels off in thin longitudinal flakes.

LEAVES : Compound, alternate, divided in 5–7 roundish leaflets 3–7 × 2–5cm., stalk 1–3cm.

FLOWERS : White, small, in axillary clusters. April-Aug.

FRUIT : Flat, oblong 1–4 seeded, pods.

Indigenous in South India. M.P. and lower Himalayan ranges. Often cultivated as a shade tree because of its dense foliage. Yields a very valuable type of hard timber, specially suitable for wood-carvings.

ROUGH LEAVED FIG

Ficus hispida Linn. *Moraceae*

Bhakada (Mar.), Badamamildi (Tel.), Daduri (Hindi), Dhed umbar (Guj.), Dumoor (Beng.), Kala umbar (Mar.), Katgular (Hindi), Karoti (Mar.), Peyatti (Mal./Tam.)

A small tree upto about 10m. high. Trunk and branches covered by hispid stiff hair.

LEAVES : Opposite (or sub-opposite) 10–25 × 5–15cm. oblong, tip elongated, margin entire or toothed, lower surface rough.

FLOWERS : Arise in fig.-like structures, 1–2cm. in diam., yellow when ripe, arising on the trunk and branches. Apr.–July.

This small tree is fairly common in poor or disturbed soil. Hollow branches and opposing leaves are peculiarities of this variety of fig.

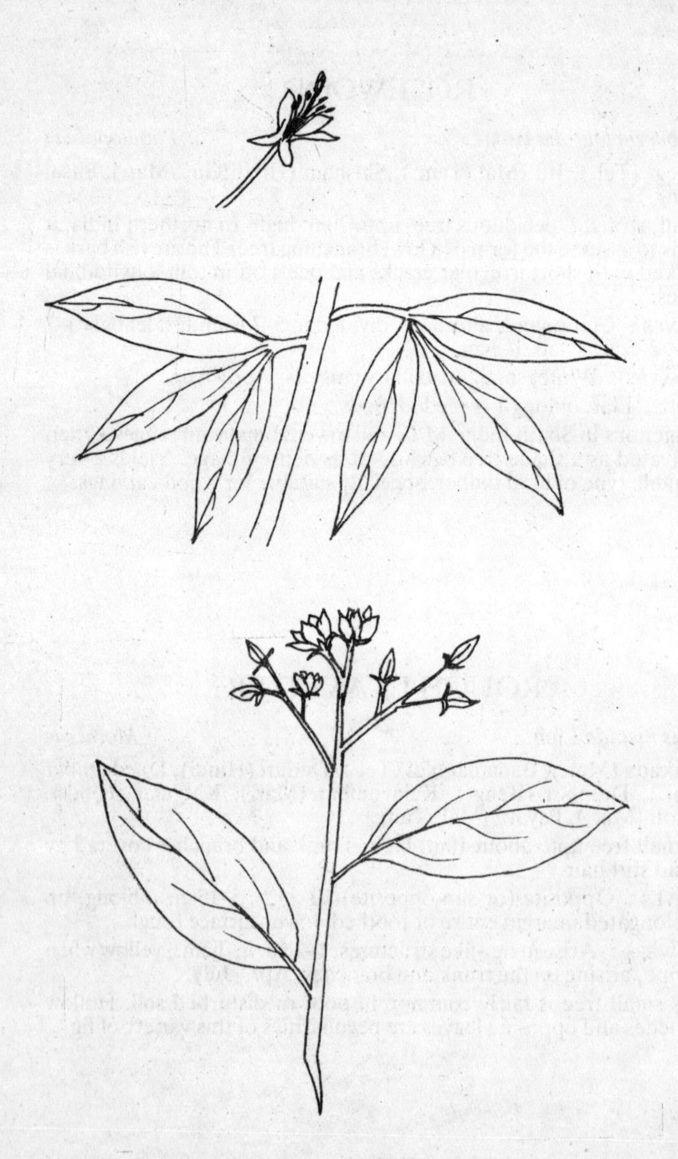

SACRED BARNA

Crataeva nurvala Buch.-Ham *Capparidaceae*
(= *C. religiosa* HK.f. & Thom.)

Barna (Hindi), Barum (Beng.), Maralingam (Tam.), Vayavarna (Mar.)

Small-sized, deciduous tree reaching upto 10m. Numerous branches.

LEAVES : Alternate, trifoliate. Main stalk 3–7cm. Leaflets oval, lance-shaped 5–7 × 3–5cm. with pointed tip. Smooth on both sides. Leaf fall occurs in cold weather. New leaves appear in Feb.–March.

FLOWERS : White turning yellow with age in dense clusters, at the ends of branches, often covering the whole tree. March-May.

FRUIT : Woody, globular, 3–5cm. in diam. on a long, jointed stalk. Seeds numerous, smooth.

Frequent in deciduous forests. Also planted near tombs or sacred places in many tropical countries.

SAL

Shorea robusta Gaertn. f. *Dipterocarpaceae*

Gugal (Tel. for resin), Maramaram (Mal.), Ral (Guj./Mar. for resin), Sal, Sakhu, Sekuva (Hindi/Beng.)

A large sub-deciduous tree, seldom quite leafless. Bark reddish-brown or grey, smooth, longitudinally fissured.

LEAVES : Simple, ovate, oblong, rounded or sometimes with an acute apex, 10–30 × 5–18cm. shining when mature, glabrous, stalk 2–5cm. high. Stipules caducous. Young leaves appear with flowers in March-April.

FLOWERS : Small, in lax, axillary panicles, pale-yellowish in colour arising in great profusion.

FRUIT : 10–15cm. ovoid, pale-yellowish or green, one-seeded with 5 somewhat unequal long wing-like persistent sepals. Seed ovoid with fleshy greenish cotyledons which contain 10–12% fatty oil.

A gregarious tree in the sub-Himalayan region; also in M.P., Orissa, U.P., Bihar upto Assam. South India also has this or allied species in moister regions. There is a prosperous trade in the seed oil as it remains solid at room temperature like Kokam oil or Cocoa butter and after processing can substitute Cocoa butter in the Chocolate industry.

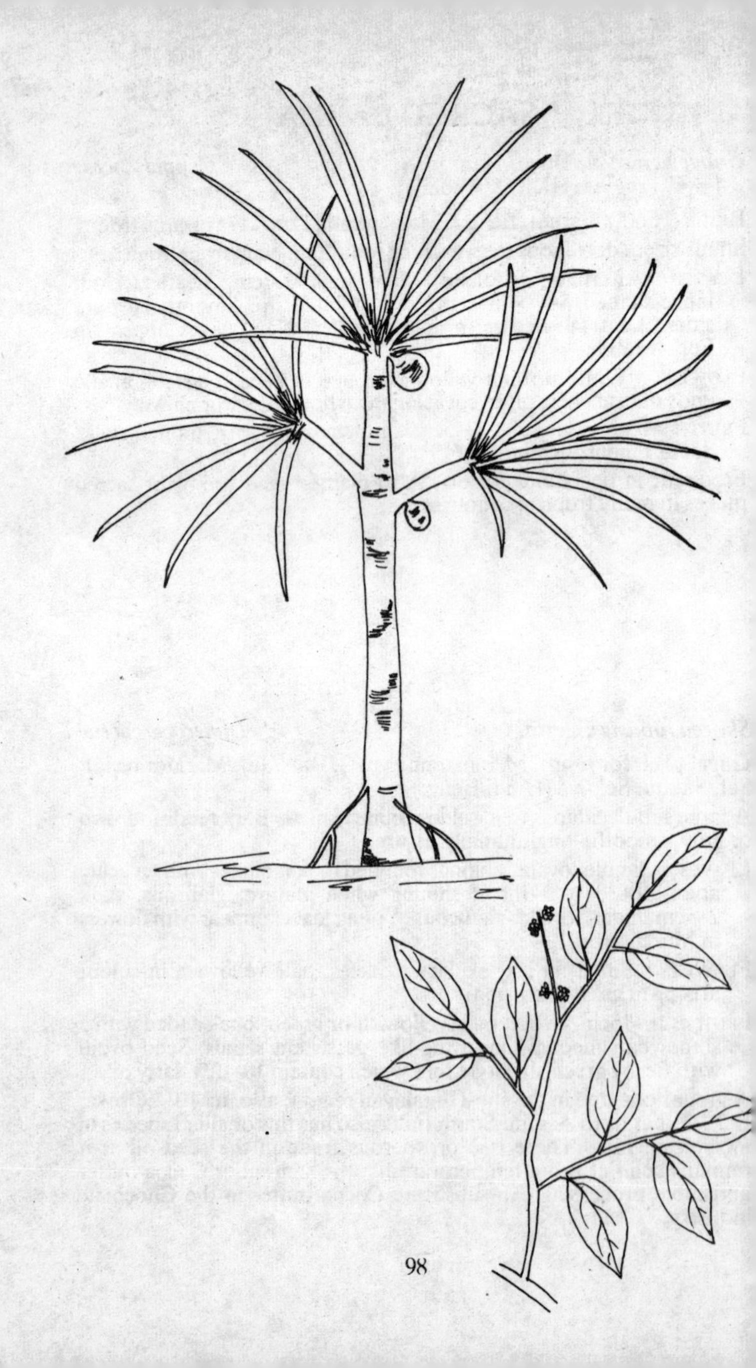

THE SCREW PINE/KEVDA

Pandanus odoratissimus Linn. *Pandanaceae*
(= *P. tectorius* Soland)

Kaida (Mal.), Ketaki, Keure, Kewra (Hindi) Kewri, Keya (Beng.), Kevada (Guj./Mar.), Mugali (Mal./Tel.), Tilai (Tam.)

Smaller but Palm-like, unisexual, evergreen trees or shrubs, densely branched at times, sometimes erect with a clear bole with a leafy crown upto 6m. high supported by aerial stilt roots.

LEAVES : Glaucous green, 1–1.8m. long, strap-shaped with long acuminate apex and spines on the margin and the mid-rib.

FLOWERS : Male flowers in the form of a loose conical spadix with numerous sub-sessile cylindrical spikes 5–10cm. long enclosed in white, fragrant spathes or boat-shaped leaves. The spadix of the female flowers is solitary, 5cm. in diam.

FRUIT : An oblong globose jointed fruit 15–25cm. in diam., yellowing in colour formed of many polygonal units.

Found along the coasts of India, growing gregariously, forming often a belt of dense impenetrable vegetation above the high tide mark. Is widespread and is recorded from Mauritius and Polynesia. Is also found growing along banks of rivers, canals, fields, ponds, etc. It is a good soil binder.

SIAMESE ROUGH BUSH

Streblus asper Lour. *Moraceae*

Barenki, Barivenkachetu (Tel.), Khareti (Mar.), Paruka (Mal.), Piraya maram (Tam.), Sehora (Beng./Hindi)

A small scraggly tree, branches rather rigid. Smooth grey bark and numerous interwoven pubescent branchlets.

LEAVES : 3–8 × 2–3cm., elliptic-ovate, acute tip, margin more or less toothed, scabrous on both surfaces when mature—like sandpaper, especially below. Stipules lanceolate, falling off early.

FLOWERS : Small, greenish, male in globose masses, female solitary. Jan.–Mar.

FRUIT : Reddish when mature, about 5cm., compressed oval, covered by a green envelope.

In deciduous forests, a well-grown tree with dark foliage offers a fine spectacle. The leaves are often used for fine polishing of wood or ivory.

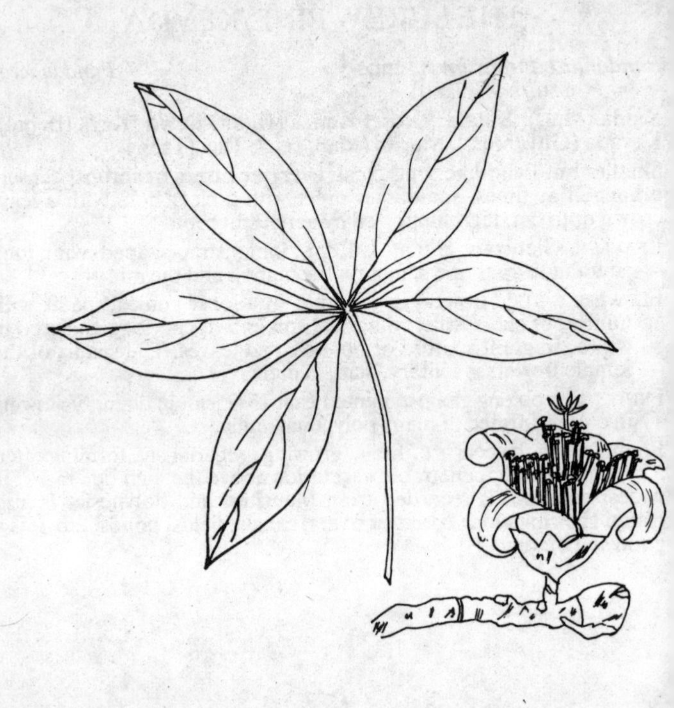

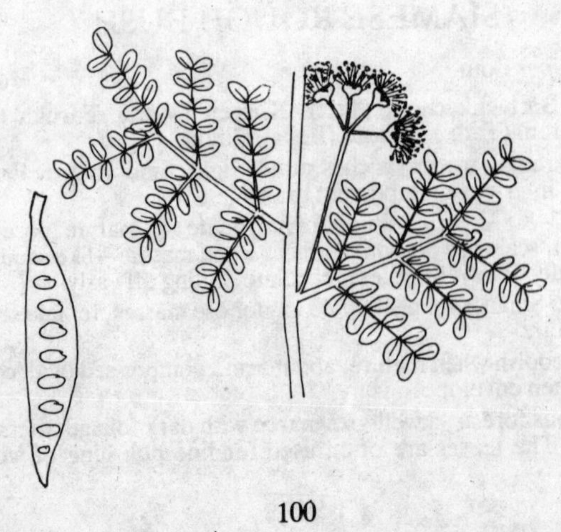

SILK COTTON

Salmalia malabarica (DC.) Schott & Endl. *Bombacaceae*
(= *Bombax malabaricum* DC.)

Booruga (Tel.), Mullilabu (Tam./Mal.), Sawar (Guj.), Semul (Hindi/Beng.), Shevri (Mar.), Simlo (Guj.)

A tall, deciduous tree upto 25m., trunk buttressed at the base, spreading branches covered with stout conical prickles. Bark pale-ash coloured, developing vertical cracks with age.

LEAVES : Alternate, with 5–7 leaflets arranged like fingers on palm (digitate), bright green.

FLOWERS : Crimson, cup-shaped, appearing at the ends of branches when the tree is leafless. Feb.–March.

FRUIT : Brownish, ovoid capsule, about 15cm. long, 5–angled, with many seeds covered with soft, silky cotton.

Common in all deciduous forests. The bright red flowers make it quite distinctive when in bloom. The flowers contain abundant nectar and are visited by a large number of noisy birds. The silky fluff floats in the air for long distances when the capsules burst open on the trees.

SIRIS

Albizzia lebbek Benth. *Mimosaceae*

Dirasana (Tel.), Siris (Hindi/Beng./Mar./Guj.), Vaga (Mal.), Vagei (Tam.)

A large deciduous tree with an umbrella-shaped crown, reaching upto 15–20m. The erect bole upto 7–10m. may reach 2m. in girth. Bark grey with irregular cracks, reddish inside.

LEAVES : Bipinnate, with a large gland on the stalk and also near the base of uppermost pinnae. Pinnae 2–3 pairs 10–12cm. long; leaflets 5 pairs, oblong, pale-green, pubescent. Leaf fall begins Oct.–Nov.

FLOWERS : White, fragrant in globose heads. March–May.

'Fair maids, the chosen of their hearts to please
Entwine their ears with Sweet Sirisha flowers'
('Shakuntala', trans. Sir M. Williams)[14]

FRUIT : Straw coloured, flat pods 10–30cm. long, bluntly pointed, thin, smooth. Seeds brown 4–12, compressed, ellipsoid.

Most of the warmer parts of India, planted on roadsides, and gardens. Popular in Sanskrit poetry.

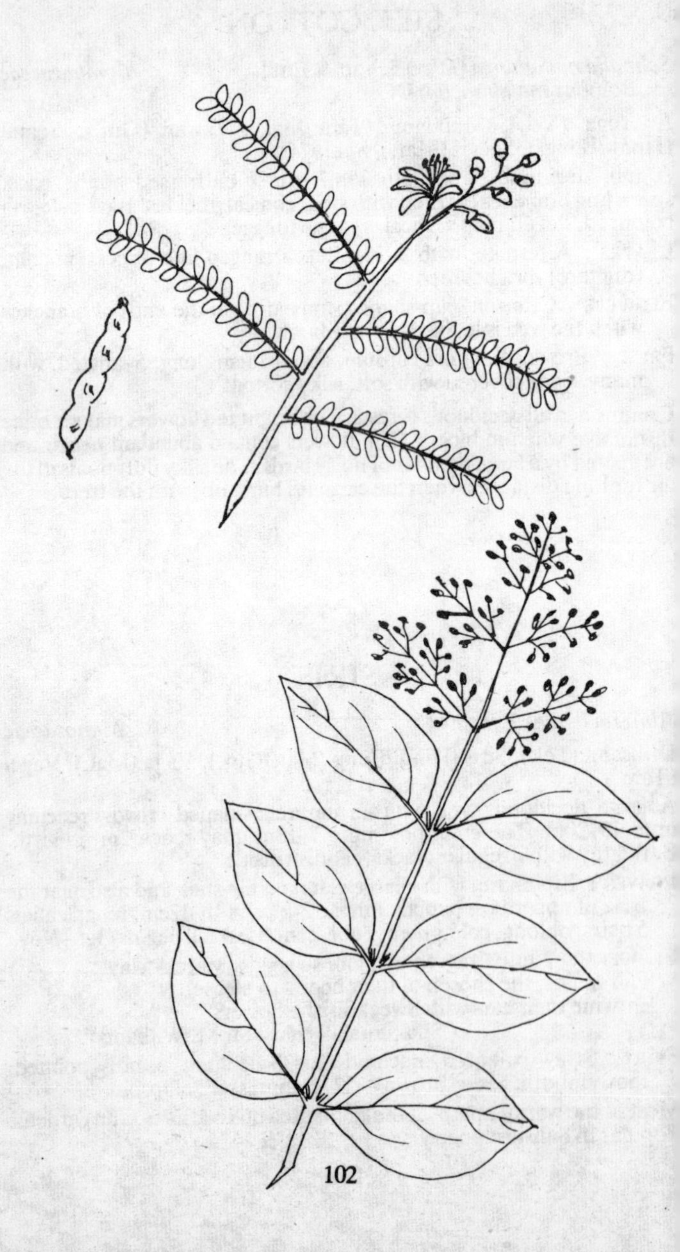

TAMARIND

Tamarindus indica Linn. *Caesalpinaceae*

Analam (Mal.), Amli, Ambli (Hindi/Guj./Beng.), Chincha (Mar.), Chintachettu (Tel.), Puli (Tam./Mal.), Tentul (Beng.)

One of the best known Indian trees. Grows to a large size (girth 42ft. recorded in Ceylon) and attains an age of over 200 years. An evergreen tree, thick, dark grey, rough bark with cracks and fissures. Branches spreading.

LEAVES : Alternate, compound, 5–12cm. long with slender, channeled axis and 10–20 pairs of nearly stalkless leaflets. When young, brilliant emerald but soon fade to jade green. Sour in taste. Stipules fall off early.

FLOWERS : Small, in loose few-flowered clusters, yellowish with pink striped petals appearing in May–June.

FRUIT : Slightly curved pod 8–20cm. long, greenish brown, sour pulp and shiny brown, squarish flattened seeds.

Commonly cultivated on roadsides as a shade tree or in villages owing to the attraction of edible sour fruits. Nothing grows under the trees owing to the acidity of its leaves. Indigenous to tropical Africa but cultivated all over the tropics.

TEAK

Tectona grandis Linn. f. *Verbenaceae*

Adaviteeku (Tel.), Sag. (Guj./Mar.), Sagun (Hindi), Segun (Beng.), Teeku (Tel.), Tekkumaram (Tam.), Thekku (Mal.)

Variable in size from 10 to 40m., young branches quadrangular, channelled; main trunk with grey-brown bark peeling in long strips.

LEAVES : Large, 30–60 × 15–30cm., elliptic with slightly pointed tip, upper surface rough, lower covered with soft hair, very young leaves when macerated impart reddish tinge to skin.

FLOWERS : Whitish, arising in short-stalked large pyramidal clusters, 30–100cm. long. June–Sept.

FRUIT : Brownish, round or 4-lobed, covered with sepals, 1–2cm.

Common in most of the deciduous forests in the plains. One of the few trees which flower during the monsoon. Timber highly prized for quality furniture.

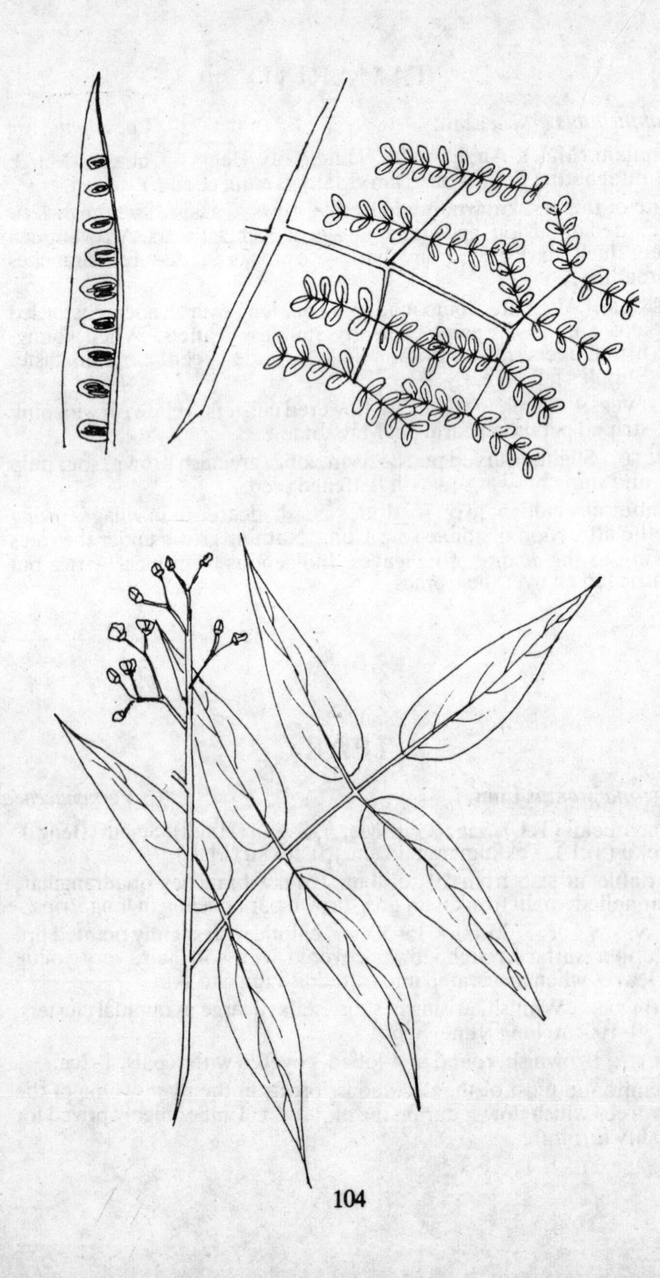

TREE OF DAMOCLES

Oroxylum indicum Vent. *Bignoniaceae*

Achi. (Tam.), Aralu (Gun./Hindi), Palagapaiyani (Mal.), Saona, Sona (Hindi/Beng.), Tentu (Guj.), Tetu (Mar.)

A deciduous medium-sized tree; trunk and branches with soft light brown bark.

LEAVES : Compound, very large, 1 to 2m., thrice branched. Leaflets 2–4 pairs 6–12cm. × 3–8cm. ovate-elliptic, with heart-shaped base and acute tip.

FLOWERS : Numerous, foetid, in a large erect pyramidal purplish cluster on a stout stalk over 50cm. long. May–July.

FRUIT : 'A long pod hanging from a branch has a weird appearance like a harlequin wand and if struck sends out a shower of large winged seeds.' (Nairne)[15]

Throughout India in deciduous forests, quite frequent.

TRUMPET FLOWER

Stereospermum personatum (Hassk) D. Chatterjee & *S. suaveolens*, DC. *Bignoniaceae*

Padal, Pader, Padri (Hindi), Padelī (Guj.), Padhri (Mar.), Padri (Tam.), Pathiri (Mal.), Tagada (Tel.)

A large tree with ascending branches upto 25m and nearly smooth greyish bark.

LEAVES : Opposite, compound with 5–9 leaflets, oval pointed 10–15 × 5–10cm.

FLOWERS : In viscous, hairy clusters, dull purple or crimson, very fragrant.

FRUIT : A long cylindrical capsule, 45–50cm. and 2cm. in diam.

Throughout moister plains and peninsular India. A tree mentioned in Sanskrit poems as blooming during the hottest season of the year (*Ritu-Samhar*, Kalidas).[16]

WILD DATE PALM

Phoenix sylvestris Roxb. *Arecaceae*

Icham (Tam.), Kejur (Beng.), Khajur (Hindi), Pedda ita (Tel.), Sendri (Mar.)

A tall palm, unbranched upto 15m. Trunk rough with persistent leaf-bases 60–75cm. broad, with a thick hemispherical crown.

LEAVES : Greyish-green, 2–3cm. long, pinnate with sharp, pointed leaflets upto 20–25cm. in length.

FLOWERS : The flowering spikes enclosed by boat-shaped bract 60–75cm. long between leaves. Male flowers yellowish-white, scented; female flowers greenish with brown tinge. Jan.–Feb.

FRUIT : Yellowish to reddish. Sweet, smaller than Iraqi dates.

Indigenous in many parts of India, common on wastelands, barren hills, either wild or cultivated. Leaves used as brooms. Yields sweet drink (Nira) which ferments into toddy.

YELLOW OLEANDER

Thevetia peruviana (Pers.) Merrill. *Apocynaceae*
(= *Thevetia neriifolia* Juss.)

Koklaphul (Beng.), Manja Arvli (Mal.), Pachaganeru (Tel.), Pachayalari (Tam.), Pili kaner (Gul./Hindi), Pivla kaner (Mar.)

A small tree, normally upto 5m. with many branches, milky, with smooth trunk, often knotted.

LEAVES : Narrow, linear, 7–8 × 0–7cm., smooth, shiny above, dull green below, arising in whorls.

FLOWERS : Yellow, bell-shaped, fragrant, 4–5cm. long, almost throughout the year.

FRUIT : Greenish, smooth like a jointed pebble.

Usually cultivated near temples or households. Thrives best in sun, easily propagated by cuttings. All parts toxic, avoided by cattle.

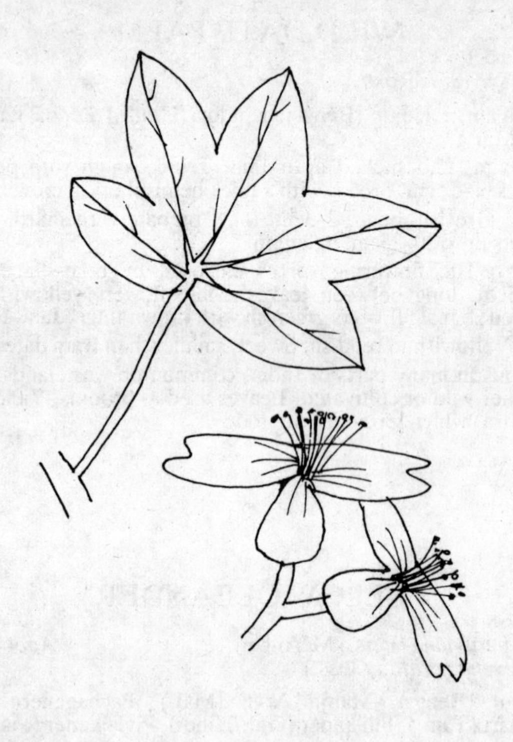

YELLOW SILK COTTON

Cochlospermum religiosum (Linn.) Alson *Cochlospermaceae*
(= *C. gossypium* DC.)

Appakutakka (Mal.), Ganeri, Ganglai (Mar.), Kumbi (Hindi), Kondagoga, Kongu (Tel.), Kongilam (Tam.)

A medium-sized tree, deciduous, upto 7–8m. high with ash-coloured bark, often abounding in transparent gum.

LEAVES : Alternate, palmately 5 lobed, 8–20cm. in diam., hairy when young but smooth when mature, leaf-stalk 10–20cm. long. Leaves begin to fall in the cold season.

FLOWERS : In terminal clusters, bright yellow 10–12cm. in diam., appearing when the tree is completely leafless, in Feb.–April. 'The blaze of a group of the trees with these flowers, tipping the naked branchlets in a golden gleam is a sight once seen never to be forgotten.' (Colthurst)[17]. The flowers are offered by the Buddhists in Ceylon for worship and is a favourite tree at the pagodas.

FRUIT : About 5–8cm. in diam., pear-shaped, splitting in 4–5 segments spilling out the seeds in May–June.

SEEDS : About 3mm. in diam., kidney-shaped, covered with white silky floss.

Conspicuous tree in the deciduous forests of India and adjoining countries of the tropics.

References

1. Sir William Jones, quoted in *The Flowering Plants of Western India* by A.K. Nairne (W.H. Allen & Co. Ltd., London, 1894), p. 98.
2. Robert Southey, quoted in Nairne, op. cit., p. 305.
3. Max Adamson, quoted in *Familiar Flowering Trees in India*, 2nd Ed., by Ida Colthurst (Thacker Spink & Co., Calcutta, 1937), p. 8.
4. The Rev. Alexander Kyd Nairne, *The Flowering Plants of Western India* (W.H. Allen & Co. Ltd., London, 1894), p. 68.
5. Sir William Hooker, quoted by Nairne, ibid., p. 6.
6. Ida Colthurst, *Familiar Flowering Trees in India*, 2nd Ed. (Thacker Spink & Co. Ltd., Calcutta, 1937), p. 50.
7. Ibid., p. 62.
8. Sir Edwin Arnold, quoted in Nairne, op. cit., p. 35.
9. Dietrich Brandis, *Indian Trees* (Constable & Co. Ltd., London, 1911).
10. From Waterfield's 'Eulogy' quoted in Colthurst, op. cit., pp. 80–81.
11. From Homer's *Odyssey*, quoted in Nairne, op. cit., p. 306.
12. Ibid.
13. Sir Edwin Arnold quoted in Nairne, op. cit., p. 177.
14. From Kalidas' *Shakuntala*, Tr. Sir Monier-Williams, quoted in Nairne, op. cit., p. 104.
15. Nairne, op. cit., p. 224.
16. From Kalidas', *Ritu-Samhara*, Tr. V.R. Nerurkar (Oriental Publishers, Bombay, 1916), pp. 7, 26; and Sir Wm. Jones, 'The Flowers are Compared to the Quiver of Kama ...', quoted in Nairne, op. cit., p. 225.
17. Colthurst, op. cit., p. 5.

GLOSSARY OF BOTANICAL TERMS

(Botanical terms used in descriptions, which are themselves separately described, have been italicized for the user's convenience.)

acuminate : Ending in a sharp, distinctly tapering point.

acute : Ending in a sharp, but not tapering point.

alternate : Where the point of attachment, as of leaves, branches, etc. is not directly opposite one another.

armed : Provided with some kind of defence, such as thorns, spines, prickles, etc.

auricle : Ear-shaped appendage, e.g. base of certain leaves.

axil : The point at which a leaf or branch diverges from the stem or *axis* to which it is attached.

axis : The main stem of a plant or a flower-cluster.

barbed : Armed with stiff *spine*-like points or bristles, usually bent backwards.

bark : The tough, outer protective covering of a woody perennial stem or root.

beaked : Ending in a prominent tip.

Belleric Myrobalan : Type of fruit yielding tannins.

bifid : Divided into two lobes by a median cleft.

berry : A few or many-seeded fleshy or pulpy fruit.

bipinnate : Twice divided, twice *compound*.

bisexual : A flower with both stamens and *pistils*.

bract : A small leaf-like, membraneous or brightly coloured organ confined to the stalks of a flower or a cluster. In the Compositae there are many smaller *bracts* surroundings a flower-head. These are known as involucral bracts. In some plants like the Bougainvillaea, the brilliantly coloured bracts are the showiest part of the flower clusters.

calyx : A collective term for all the *sepals* of a flower.

capsule : A dry fruit with more than one compartment which splits open.

cluster : An indefinite designation for *inflorescence*.

compound : Composed of two or more similar parts united into one whole, as in the separate leaflets of a compound leaf.

cordate	: Heart-shaped.
corolla	: The petals, collectively, of a flower. They may be separate or united.
cotyledon	: Simple embryonic leaf in seed-bearing plants.
crenate	: Shallowly toothed with rounded teeth.
deciduous	: Dropping its leaves, petals, fruits, etc.
dentate	: Toothed, with the teeth more or less perpendicular to the margin of the leaf.
digitate	: resembling a spread hand, e.g. leaflets of a compound leaf.
dioecious	: Having male and female flowers on separate plants.
downy	: Softly and weakly hairy
drupe	: A fleshy or pulpy one-seeded fruit that does not split. The seed is enclosed in a bony stone, hence these fruits are sometimes called stoned fruits, e.g. Mango.
elliptic	: Egg-shaped.
epidermis	: The outermost layer of cells.
exfoliate	: Shed its outermost layer.
flower	: An absolutely essential organ in all seeding plants. Flowers are the seats of all sexual activity in flowering plants.
foetid	: Having a stale, nauseating smell.
frond	: The leaf of ferns and palms.
fruit	: The ripened *ovary* and the seeds within or upon it, together with other parts of the flower which change materially in the process of ripening.
galls	: abnormal outgrowth in plant tissue caused by a parasite.
glabrous	: Smooth, lacking in hairs or any sort of roughness or *pubescence*.
gland	: An organ or surface of secretion. Unicellular or multicellular hairs may be glandular.
glaucous	: Covered with a bluish or whitish bloom which rubs off.
globose	: Globular.
glomerate	: In dense globe-shaped compact clusters.
gregarious	: Growing close together.
habitat	: A site.
hispid	: Clothed with rigid or bristly hairs.

hoary	: Covered with greyish or whitish hairs.
imparipinnate	: A *pinnate* leaf which has an odd terminal leaflet.
inflorescence	: A flower cluster.
Kapok	: Silky fibre used for stuffing mattresses, sleeping bags, etc
labiate	: Lipped.
laticiferous	: Containing a milky sap.
lanceolate	: Shaped like the blade of a lance—several times longer than wide.
latex	: Milky sap.
leaf	: The foliage organ of most flowering plants.
leaflet	: One of the ultimate segments of a compound leaf.
leaf-stalk	: A *petiole*.
legume	: A pod or fruit that splits into two halves and has the seeds attached to the lower seam.
lobed	: Which has rounded segments extending less than half-way to the centre or midrib. If the division extends more than that the organ is better described as divided.
macerated	: Soften or separate due to soaking.
membranous	: Thin, transparent and pliable sheet, usually of fibrous tissue.
mucilage	: Sticky liquid secreted by certain plants.
node	: The point of a stem at which leaves normally appear.
nut	: A hard-shelled, single-celled, single-seeded fruit that does not split.
obconic	: Inversely conic, i.e. which has attachment at the apex.
oblong	: Longer than broad with nearly parallel sides.
obovate	: Inversely ovate, i.e. the broadest part furthest away from the stalk.
obovoid	: A solid with an inversely oval outline.
obcordate	: Inversely heart-shaped.
obtuse	: Leaf with a rounded or blunt tip.
opposite	: Having the point of attachment, as of leaves, twigs, etc., precisely opposite each other.
orbicular	: Circular.
oval	: Broadly *elliptic*
ovary	: The *ovule*-bearing part of the *pistil*.

ovate : Egg-shaped with the broader end downwards.

ovoid : A solid with an *oval* outline.

ovule : The structure which after fertilization becomes the seed.

palmate : Referring to a leaf radially *lobed*, divided or ribbed like the fingers of a hand.

panicle : A loose, open flower cluster which blooms from the centre or bottom towards the edges or top. The main stalk is never terminated by a flower.

paripinnate : Evenly *pinnate* as a pinnate leaf ending in two leaflets.

peduncle : Stalk of a plant bearing an *inflorescence* or a solitary flower.

perianth : The floral envelope commonly used for flowers in which there is no clear distinction between *corolla* and *calyx*.

petal : One of the leaves of the *corolla*.

petiole : Leaf-stalk.

pinnate : With leaflets or veins arranged as are the segments of a bird's feather, on each side of a common stalk.

pinnatifid : *Pinnately* cut or divided into segments.

pistil : The seed-bearing organ of the flower consisting of *ovary, stigma* and, when present, style.

plumose : Feathery, having fine hairs on each side.

pod : Any dry elongated fruit that splits along one or two seams.

pollen : The grains containing the male element necessary to ensure fertilization, found in the anther.

pollination : Transfer of the pollen from the anthers to the *stigma*.

prickle : A small, weak, spiny outgrowth.

pubescent : Denoting hairiness but referring in particular to short, soft hair.

raceme : An elongated flower-cluster blooming from the bottom upward with a single main stalk from which arise the stalks of several flowers.

receptacle : The much-modified stem end which bears the organs of a flower or the collected florets of a head.

rib : A nerve or vein in a leaf. The midrib is the main one.

ot : Part of the plant bearing neither leaves nor reproduction organs but provided with an apical growing point and functioning as an organ of absorption, aeration, food-storage, etc.

sette : A cluster of closely crowded radiating leaves appearing to arise from the ground.

fous : Reddish-brown.

abrous : Rough to the touch.

ed : The ripened, fertilized ovule of a flower, consisting of the embryo and its proper coats.

pal : One of the leaves of the *calyx*.

rrated : Which has sharp, saw-like teeth pointing forward on the margin.

ssile : Without a stalk.

eath : A tubular organ which surrounds the base of a stalk, as in grasses, or helps to form one.

rub : It is difficult to make a distinction between a tree and a shrub. Generally a shrub is a low, woody plant that has several stems instead of a trunk as most trees have.

adix : A conical *inflorescence* bearing many small stalkless flowers on a fleshy stalk which is covered by a *spathe*.

athe : Large *bract* enclosing an *inflorescence*.

nple : Not branched, not compound.

ine : A sharp, woody outgrowth from the stem.

men : One of the anther-bearing organs of a flower.

inous : Having *spines*

m : The main axis of a plant capable of bearing leaves and flowers, as distinguished from the *axis*-bearing roots.

gma : That part of the *pistil* which receives the pollen.

oule : A small paired leaf-like outgrowth occurring at the base of a leaf or its stalk.

o-ovoid : Egg-shaped.

culent : Juicy, fleshy, soft and thickened.

carp : A collective fruit.

dril : A slender prolongation of the stem or leaf by means of which a plant clings to a support.

ninal : At the end.

nentose : *Pubescent*, with dense entangled woolly or cottony hair.

tree : A woody plant which normally produces o main trunk and a more or less distinct and cleav head.

trifoliate : With three leaflets to the main stalk.

umbel : Umbrella-shaped *inflorescence* in which flow arise from the same point in the main stem a have stalks of the same length to form a clus with the youngest flowers at the centre.

venation : The arrangement of nerves or veins in a leaf other organ.

whorl : Radial arrangement of petals, leaves, etc. aro a stem.

Suggested Additional Reading

Benthall, A.P., *The Trees of Calcutta and its Neighbourhoo* Calcutta, 1946.

A comprehensive reference work with some illustrations.

Blatter, Ethelbert, *The Palms of British India and Ceylon*, OU Bombay, 1926.

Cooke, Theodore, *The Flora of the Presidency of Bombay*, 3 vol (Reprinted) Calcutta, 1967.

An un-illustrated reference work, based on a Key, providing inf mation on the identification of trees from field specimens of twi leaves, flowers, etc.

Cowen, D.V., *Flowering Trees and Shrubs of India*, Bombay, 195

Written in the language of the layman and illustrated, it provi fascinating glimpses into the folklore and mythology surround particular trees and valuable information about their econor uses.

Hooker, J.D., *The Flora of British India*, 7 vols., London, 1875– Dehra Dun, 1982.

A very informative, comprehensive reference work.

Manjunath, D.L., B.N. Shastri, A. Krishnamurti, Y.R. Chadha a S.B. Deshprabhu (eds.), *The Wealth of India*, 11 volumes, CSI New Delhi, 1948–1976.

A very comprehensive reference work of much value.

Mc Cann, C., *Hundred Beautiful Trees of India, a Descriptive Pictorial Book*, Calcutta, 1959.

Santapau, H., *Common Trees*, New Delhi, 1966.

Description of individual trees in layman's language with illustratio

Index

NOTES

NOTES

NOTES

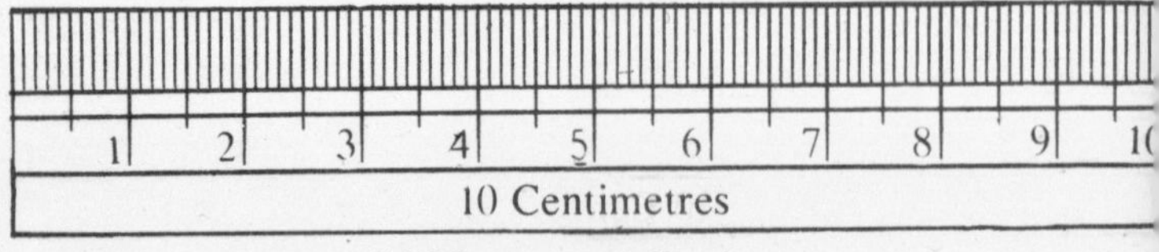

1/10 Metre, or 1 Decimetre

METRIC SYSTEM AND EQUIVALENTS IN ENGLISH SYSTEM

Centimetres	Inches	Inches	Centimetres
1	0.4	1	2.5
2	0.8	2	5.1
3	1.2	3	7.6
4	1.6	4	10.1
5	2.0	5	12.7
6	2.4	6	15.2
7	2.8	7	17.8
8	3.1	8	20.3
9	3.5	9	22.9
10	3.9	10	25.4

1 foot = 3 decimetres

1 metre = 3.3. feet